GEORGE KIRKLEY

Weight Lifting and Weight Training

A-29

BELL PUBLISHING COMPANY • NEW YORK

Contents

List of Illustrations

CHAPTER ONE

Principles of weight training

MOST men cherish a desire to have a well-developed body, even if very few of them take the trouble to do anything about it, but those who do train for the purpose of improved health, strength and development are wise. Wise because one of the most important things in life is good health. Good health is not necessarily combined with large muscles, of course ; one can be very healthy indeed with only a slight musculature, but good health plus good development is something even better. So why not seek that as well?

Muscular development can be had without using weights for the purpose. One can practise wrestling, gymnastics and many other forms of physical activity and, in addition to the enjoyment of the sport, can often make noticeable muscular gains, but for those who want the maximum development weight training is the best method. It can be scientifically planned – unlike the playing of games or the participation in sports, when the acquirement of skills and enjoyment of the game are the primary objectives and the muscular benefits merely incidental.

Weight lifting can also be made progressive, by the gradual increasing of resistance as the muscles grow in size and strength. Indeed the principle of progressive resistance is a major factor in weight training. The right exercises and other factors are essential, but unless the work is progressive – which means that it must lead to constant handling of heavier and heavier poundages – the realization of one's potential will not come.

The use of a muscle against resistance causes an increase in size. This growth is due in part to improved circulation of blood and also to chemical conditions arising out of contraction. Activity causes some destruction of the constituents of the muscle but when nature replaces the lost materials she overcompensates.

Almost without exception the world's best developed men have used progressive resistance exercises to build their physique and they have used heavier and heavier weights as they got bigger and stronger. The variety of exercises is very wide and dozens of different movements can be performed to build the physique in a harmonious and effective manner. Moreover, in this process the general health is improved and the vital organs function with greater efficiency.

Amount of Exercise

Generally, a training session should consist of a sufficient number of exercises to build all-round development, with at least one exercise for every major body part – particularly for a beginner, who usually lacks all-over development. Later, graduation can be made to exercises that are essential for the building up of those parts of the body that are below the over-all standard.

A training session should last, on an average, anything from an hour to an hour and a half. This is sufficient time to get through enough work for our purpose. The number of exercises will average from eight to fifteen, depending on one's immediate object. At certain times, one may use only five or six movements for a special purpose. At others, double that number.

Frequency of Training

Since resistance exercise breaks down muscular tissue, which nature replaces and the process begins immediately after exercising, a rest period is essential to allow nature to do her work. Generally, it is not wise to exercise with weights every day and for most people a rest period of two days has been found to be the best. This means training sessions every other day, which is a good general principle. So aim at three or four sessions weekly, depending on such factors as your own personal recuperative powers and the time you have available for training.

Many people, too, find it beneficial to train hard and consistently for a period of, say, six months, then have a lay-off for about two weeks, before continuing again for another six-months' period.

After the beginner's stage, when a standard body-building course has been followed, perhaps for several months, you will know a lot more about your own particular physical and recuperative powers and will be able to plan your own future schedules and methods of training, bearing in mind that the essential basic principles must be maintained.

Any variation from these principles of progression, frequency of training, rest periods, number of repetitions, etc., depends entirely on the individual – his own powers, ambitions, intelligence, enthusiasm and adaptability.

You must not be afraid to experiment or to depart from the accepted path if by doing so, better results ensue.

Repetitions

The number of repetitions for any exercise can vary quite considerably, depending on the individual, his physical type, the nature of the exercise and the object in view. Later chapters will give more detailed aspects of this important factor of weight training. Generally, the number of repetitions will range from as little as three to as many as thirty, although the average for most exercises will be around eight to ten.

For general physique building where one is not concerned with increased strength so much as increased muscle size, the repetitions should be fairly high – generally from eight to twelve for most movements. The high repetitions allow a longer period for the muscles to be flushed with blood and tend to increase the size of the muscle as opposed to increasing its strength. Lower repetitions, while still in part achieving the object of increasing muscle size, tend to have more effect on increasing strength. This is why weight-lifters rarely perform high repetitions in their training, but instead use heavier weights and fewer repetitions.

The importance of physical type must be considered, too – more so in body building than in weight lifting – particularly as in weight lifting a good proportion of the participants are those of a physical type that is most favourable for the sport.

The next chapter deals in greater detail with this subject.

CHAPTER TWO

Physical types

ALL men are born with different physical characteristics and potentialities – and in the world of physical-culture various authorities have made long and careful studies of the different anatomic types.

Perhaps the most famous of these authorities is Doctor Sheldon, an American who went to extreme lengths in scientific research to categorize human beings.

Broadly, he has divided men into three main types, or groups. Few men, of course, belong predominantly to any of the three types; few are extreme examples of the two outer groups. But the vast majority have quite easily-discernible bodily tendencies or characteristics, and a knowledge of them can determine a man's potential and the best methods of training to attain maximum bodily development.

In the body-building sphere it has been proved that different types need different training methods to achieve maximum results. Further, the physical type of a man governs largely what particular sport or athletic pursuit he will be best suited for.

For example, the heavy, globular individual, who is destined naturally to achieve heavy girths, cannot ever hope to excel as a marathon runner – but he may well become successful at heavy athletics.

Ectomorph Type
Sheldon's first anatomic type is the thin man: an individual characterized by his deep thorax and restricted abdominal area. He is generally light-boned, with slender musculature and is essentially suited to such pursuits as cycling and middle to long-distance running.

He can, of course, make good progress at body building or weight lifting, although he will rarely win championships in these spheres. And he will have to work many times harder for his gains than one who is better equipped physically.

Sheldon is emphatic that nothing can alter the physical

destiny of the ectomorph, but my experience in body building has shown me that persistent and correct training in the formative stages can transform one of this type into a well-built and strongish man, although perhaps not to the extent of winning championships and other major honours.

Endomorph Type

At the other end of the anatomic scale there is the endomorph: thick-boned, often fleshy and with a large abdominal area.

This individual tends to put on weight easily. Obviously he is not suited to such activities as cycling or running, but can excel at many of the slower types of strength feats in weight lifting.

His large abdominal area, with its longer-than-average intestine, means that he can absorb the maximum nourishment from his food, a dominant factor in bodyweight increase. He responds to heavy training, can make great gains in the minimum time, but has difficulty in moulding a shapely and hard, muscular physique.

Mesomorph Type

This is the middle or intermediate type. He belongs to the group from which a large proportion of weight-lifting and body-building champions arise, and is particularly likely to become a champion if he has predominant endomorph tendencies.

His physical proportions will be the most pleasing of all the types; his mobility and musculature eminently suitable to excel at most athletic strength feats.

No individual with ambitions in any particular physical sphere need be discouraged if he discovers that he is attempting something 'out of his class'.

The ectomorph *can* put on weight and increase his muscular size. The endomorph need *not* be a shapeless bulk. But it is extremely unlikely that an extreme ectomorph will ever win a world weight-lifting title or a Mr. Universe contest. No extreme endomorph is ever likely to win an Olympic 10,000 metres or marathon title.

But *everyone,* no matter what his type, can improve his health, strength and physique if he is ambitious enough and prepared to work hard and consistently.

The road will be hard for some – particularly those at the extreme ends of the anatomic scale. But progress is certain if the right methods are used.

The teenager starting out on the trail to seek honours as a weight lifter or body builder will be all the better equipped if he knows at the onset that his ambitions will be governed to a large extent by his physical type.

If he is an extreme ectomorph or endomorph, he will know that his chances of top honours are more remote than those of the more fortunate types. But if he feels that the rewards of self-improvement are worth more, in the long run, than championship honours, he will at least begin with no illusions.

The fundamental principle of type-training is low repetitions with high resistance for the ectomorph, and high repetitions with low resistance for the endomorph.

The late George Walsh, noted British authority and instructor on this method of training, carried out numerous experiments with his many pupils – and his successes were positive indication that he worked on the right lines.

Extreme and near-extreme ectomorphs thrive best on a training routine consisting of a few exercises only, involving not more than four or five consecutive repetitions, with resistances ranging from 75 per cent to 95 per cent of maximum ability for one single movement.

At the opposite end of the scale, the extreme and near-extreme endomorphs thrive best on routines consisting of a large number of exercises – maybe as many as fifteen or twenty – involving high repetitions with resistances ranging from 30 per cent to 60 per cent of maximum ability.

In between these extreme ranges lies the greater majority of body builders and the scale of repetitions, and resistances generally, need readjusting to an 'in between' range.

A knowledge of the principles of type training will enable the novice bodybuilder to avoid much trial-and-error training at the start of his career. Even so, it is by no means certain that he will immediately hit upon the ideal routine for his own particular needs, though he can be sure that he won't pursue a path that deviates much from his own ideal route to success.

First, he will need to determine his anatomic type. My brief description earlier on will help but his self analysis should be supplemented, if possible, by the help of someone who has good experience of this method of training.

Weight training for body building has been proved to be easily the best means of development. And no matter what physical type a man is, or how weak and undeveloped he is – provided he has no organic defects – he can make improvement. Even if he merely follows a standard course without bothering about his physical type.

Everyone can improve to some degree. The best gains will be made by those who have the best natural potential, the highest degree of ambition and determination, pursue their objective with the greatest zest and enthusiasm – and who follow the training routine most suitable for their physical type.

CHAPTER THREE

How the muscles work

ALTHOUGH it isn't essential for the body builder to have an
expert knowledge of kinesiology (muscle mechanics) it is useful
to have some knowledge of the functions of the muscular
system, where the muscles are located, and their names.

The accompanying charts, showing the major muscles, will
be a useful guide in this respect.

In the human body there are three kinds of muscle: VOL-
UNTARY, INVOLUNTARY and CARDIAC.

The voluntary muscles are our main concern, those which
we can move or control by positive thought and action. The
involuntary muscles are mainly found in the internal organs,
such as the stomach and intestines. The cardiac muscles are
related to the heart.

Actually there are more than 500 muscles, most of them
arranged in pairs, on each side of the body, but the body
builder is concerned with only about a tenth of this number.

The muscles are comprised of long cells of protoplasm, arranged in thin fibres of various length. Each fibre is surrounded
by a sheath called the sarcolemma. A number of these fibres
are bundled together and again covered by a sheath of connective tissue, the perimysium. Further, a number of these
bundles are grouped together by more connective tissue, the
epimysium.

Each muscle has a blood supply and a motor nerve, which
provides the action of movement. Movement is made either by
the will or reflex (involuntary) action.

Muscular tissue has the ability to contract (shorten) and
return to its original length – in other words it has elasticity.
In the action of contraction, the fibres shorten and thicken.

The action of exercising a muscle, alternately contracting
and returning to original length, flushes it with blood and
thickens the fibres in time. It also, of course, strengthens the
muscle.

The muscles are attached to bone and have an *origin* and
an *insertion*. Each end of a muscle has a *tendon* for attachment

to the bone. The tendon itself is not elastic, neither does it have a blood supply.

The tendon attached to the fixed or more stabilized bone is called the *origin* ; the other tendon, fixed to the moving bone, is its *insertion*. Sometimes a muscle is attached to another muscle in order to strengthen or supplement the action of that muscle.

When a muscle contracts it will pull the two bones to which it is attached closer together. For example, when you perform a curling movement, the forearm is pulled towards the upper arm by the contraction of the brachialis and biceps.

Each muscle passes over and activates a joint and in some cases muscles act on two joints.

A muscle does not perform any actual work unless the origin and insertion approach each other.

The muscles are of various shapes and generally take their names from the shape or structure, situation, etc.; e.g. biceps (two-headed), triceps (three-headed) pronator-quadratus (square), pectoralis major (large muscle of the chest).

A muscle can contract in three ways. (It is never quite relaxed – there must always be some slight tension in order to bind the joints together and stop them from dislocating.)

First, there is *concentric* contraction, in which the muscle works or shortens against a resistance, as in curling a weight.

Then there is *eccentric* contraction, in which the muscle returns to its original length against a resistance, as in returning the forearm to its original position after curling, the brachialis and biceps lowering it by slowly relaxing.

The third is *isometric* contraction, in which the muscle will not lengthen but remains in a state of static contraction, as in muscle control, alternately hardening and relaxing the muscle.

There are four purposes for which a muscle can contract. It can work as (*a*) a *prime mover,* (*b*) an *antagonist,* (*c*) a *fixator,* or (*d*) a *synergist.*

The muscles that actually perform a movement, as for example, the brachialis and biceps when flexing the elbow, are *prime movers.* As they contract, their *antagonists* (in this case, the triceps) help the prime mover to act by gradually relaxing.

Another muscle can help the prime mover – the synergist. For example, the biceps also supinates (turns) the forearm and

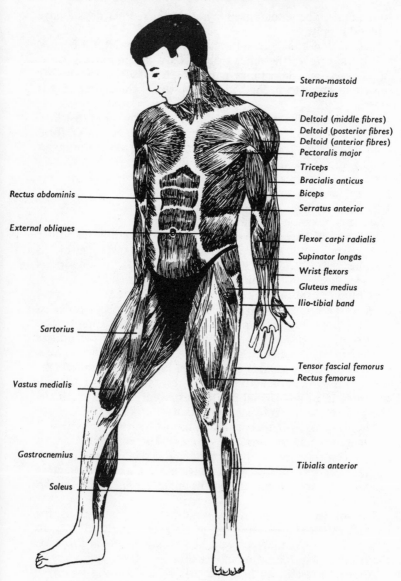

Sterno-mastoid
Trapezius
Deltoid (middle fibres)
Deltoid (posterior fibres)
Deltoid (anterior fibres)
Pectoralis major
Triceps
Bracialis anticus
Biceps
Serratus anterior
Flexor carpi radialis
Supinator longus
Wrist flexors
Gluteus medius
Ilio-tibial band
Tensor fascial femorus
Rectus femorus
Tibialis anterior

Rectus abdominis
External obliques
Sartorius
Vastus medialis
Gastrocnemius
Soleus

THE MUSCULAR SYSTEM (front view)

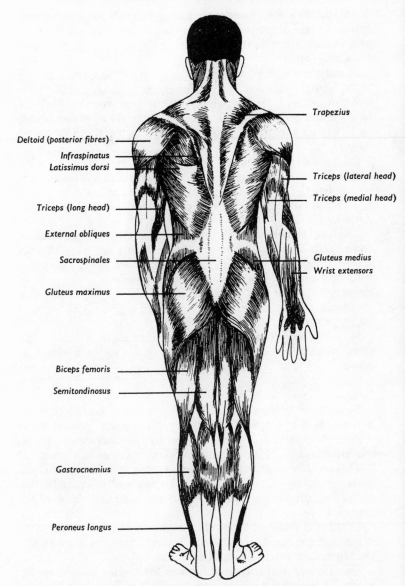

Trapezius

Deltoid (posterior fibres)

Infraspinatus

Latissimus dorsi

Triceps (lateral head)

Triceps (medial head)

Triceps (long head)

External obliques

Sacrospinales

Gluteus medius

Wrist extensors

Gluteus maximus

Biceps femoris

Semitondinosus

Gastrocnemius

Peroneus longus

THE MUSCULAR SYSTEM (rear view)

flexes the shoulder. If you want to flex your elbow without performing these other actions, then the pronators of the forearm and the extensors of the shoulder must work also to inhibit these movements.

A muscle can hold a part steady so that other muscles can work from it – this is a *fixator*. For example, the rectus abdominus can act as a fixator when you are performing a straight legs' raising movement when lying on the floor, by steadying and holding the pelvis, from which some of the hip flexors work.

All muscles have a normal range of movement.

A *full-range* movement is the contraction of a muscle over its full length: that is, from fully contracted to fully stretched.

This full range is divided into outer, middle and inner ranges. An example of this is when curling a weight.

The movement from the start of the curl, with the arms straight, to a point just before the forearms are parallel with the floor, is the *outer range*. From here, to a point where the forearms are just above the parallel position, is the *middle range*. And from this point to the conclusion of the curling movement, with the forearms fully flexed on the upper arms, is the *inner range*.

It will be seen that in this example, the muscles have to exert their greatest force to overcome the resistance in the middle range.

Levers

Some weight lifters and body builders talk of certain of their lifts as being leverage lifts. Actually, all lifts are leverage lifts.

All movements that can be made by the body are leverage movements, as each set of muscle, joint or bones, is a lever.

There are three orders of lever and these apply to the human body in the same way as to engineering and science. In the body, the bones are *levers*, the joints *fulcrums* and the muscles the *force*.

In the first order of levers (the lever of stability), the fulcrum is between the resistance and the power. Examples in everyday life are the seesaw, or a pair of scissors.

An example of this type of lever in the human body is in the action of bending the head backwards. The joint between the spinal column and the cranium is the fulcrum ; the weight of the head, the front of the fulcrum, is the resistance, and the upper fibres of the trapezius muscle, inserted in the back of the skull, is the power.

In the second order of levers (the lever of *power*), the resistance is between the power and the fulcrum. Everyday examples are a crowbar and a wheelbarrow (in which the wheel is the fulcrum).

An example in the human body is rising on the toes. The contact of the toes on the floor is the fulcrum, the weight of the body is the resistance, and the calf muscles are the power.

On the third order of levers, the power is between the fulcrum and the resistance.

An everyday example is a man raising a ladder from the ground by pulling on one of the lower rungs.

An example in the human body is raising the trunk from a bent-over position. The hip-joint is the fulcrum, the weight of the trunk is the resistance, and the glutei muscles, attached to the pelvis, is the power.

The relation of the power arm to the resistance arm determines the strength provided by a lever. The longer the power arm the greater the force that can be exerted.

In the human body most of the levers are of the third order, and generally work at a mechanical disadvantage. One would be much stronger if the majority of human levers were of the second order.

This chapter is by no means a complete treatise on the subject of muscles, which is a specialized subject and would fill much more space than I have available, but I hope I have said enough to enable you to have a better understanding of the muscular system and to appreciate the purpose of the various body-building movements.

CHAPTER FOUR

Eating for health and strength

THERE is no doubt that a man's food is one of the most important things in his life. Like breathing and sleeping, it is something we cannot do without, and, in effect, we are what we eat.

We need food from the moment we are born until the day we die, yet it is amazing how most people pay little regard to what they eat. They will take extreme care over choosing a new suit, a camera or a car. But often little or no thought is given to the very thing that keeps them alive. For, make no mistake about it, the choice of the right food can make all the difference between average health and the very much rarer robust, abounding health, and for the physical culturist and the body builder, diet is just as important as training.

Food affects the nutrition of the largest muscle and the thinnest fibre. It affects the quality of blood and the health of the skin. In fact, every body process is ultimately dependent on food for its efficient functioning.

Sound nutrition demands a balanced diet, in which all the essential nutrients are present in adequate quantities.

Calories

First, let us consider calories. A calorie is a unit of energy, and an average man needs about 1,800 daily just to keep the basic functions of life ticking over – the heart-beat, the lung expansion and recoil, the digestive processes and so on. In addition, he needs extra calories for walking about, working and other physical activities and the more strenuous his work or activities, the more calories he needs.

The most important aspect of eating is: take in enough of the right foods.

We need protein for rebuilding body cells which are constantly being destroyed and the body builder, with his more-than-average amount of exercise, needs protein much more than the man who rarely exercises.

We need fat, as a reserve source of energy and for warmth; carbohydrate for energy; mineral salts to regulate body processes ; vitamins to ensure the efficient absorption of food and for protective functions ; and, of course, water.

We get protein from flesh foods: meat, game and poultry ; also from eggs, cheese, butter, milk, etc.

Animal protein as we eat it is not really suitable for use in building up human tissue, but is converted during digestion into a form acceptable to the human body. This involves changes in chemical structure, the final result being an aggregation of amino-acids (the basic form of protein constituents) which are used by the body as required.

Generally, flesh foods are richer than vegetable protein.

During heavy exercise the need for protein is increased. The size of a man, too, determines his need for protein. The larger he is, the more he needs.

Carbohydrate is the principal energy food and includes starches and sugars – such things as oatmeal, syrup, bread, potatoes and dates – and provides about the same number of calories to the ounce as protein.

The digestive processes ultimately convert all sugar and starch into glucose (blood sugar), in which form it enters the blood stream for distribution to the muscles.

When very arduous or lengthy exercise is being undertaken it is advisable to increase your intake of glucose or sugar. Take this on the day before the event, making the last meal an evening one, with plenty of carbohydrate, preferably about two hours before retiring for the night to enable it to digest properly before going to sleep.

During sleep this extra energy will be stored in the muscles and liver. A good breakfast will increase the store ; then take a light lunch before your event or session of activity.

Fat is contained in such foods as butter, eggs, cheese, nuts, meat and fish.

The maximum assimilation of fat does not occur for about six hours, so it is not an ideal nutrient for quick energy – despite its high caloric content.

Remember, too, that for complete combustion of fat, carbohydrate must be present, or else acidosis may result.

Vitamins

Vitamins have a marked influence on health, and while most

of us get enough to remain free from the worst effects of vitamin deficiencies most adults do not get enough.

There are far too many people who lack the energy, vitality and positive health that only vitamin saturation promotes.

You can get vitamins in their synthesized and pure form, but it is much better to get them by eating plenty of the vitamin-rich foods. By doing so you also get other nutrients. Food chemists have isolated a whole alphabet of vitamins, but by concentrating on the half-dozen or so major ones, you will get all you need.

Vitamin A is essential for growth and plays an important part in the way the eyes react to light. It also performs a protective function in the skin, particularly in connection with the mucous membranes of the eyes, respiratory tract and throat. The body can store this vitamin, too, if it gets more than it needs at the time.

Certain fats and fatty foods contain this vitamin, but the most potent source is found in halibut-liver oil ; after that, cod-liver oil. Other good sources are in carrots, spinach, ox liver, dried apricots, peaches and butter.

In terms of health and strength, the most significant of the vitamins is the *B group*, called 'B complex', which are essential for healthy nerves, sturdy growth and the release of energy from carbohydrate food.

The harder you work the more B_1 you need. Include in your diet plenty of wholemeal bread, beef, mutton, liver, kidney, green peas, oatmeal, bacon and milk. White bread has a poor vitamin B content and sugar none at all.

Vitamin C is essential to keep the tissues firm and elastic and the body young and agile. Poor energy, vague ill-health, sallow complexion, restlessness and a run-down feeling are all indications of a lack of Vitamin C.

Eat plenty of fresh fruit and vegetables each day. Don't live largely on cooked and prepared foods ; otherwise you will not be getting enough Vitamin C. Much of this vitamin is lost through cooking processes.

Vitamin D puts calcium and phosphorus to work in making good bones, teeth and tissue, keeps the heart strong and the nerves resilient.

Spend a little time each day, whenever possible, sunbathing.

Your skin contains a complex substance which works with sunlight to provide your Vitamin D. In the winter, or when it isn't possible to sunbathe, use a sun lamp, or take a fish-liver oil concentrate. In your food you get this vitamin in eggs, milk, butter and mushrooms.

Weight Control

If you eat more food than is required for energy purposes, the surplus is stored as fat and remains as such until it is removed by either increased exercising or by dieting.

If not enough food is taken for energy purposes, then body flesh is consumed to provide energy and the bodyweight is reduced.

If your food intake is balanced with your energy output, then your bodyweight is kept steady.

Losing weight by means of exercise is not too easy and some form of dieting is essential.

The first step is to reduce your total calorie intake by cutting down on some of the carbohydrate foods such as chocolate, sweets, pastry and shop cakes. In any case, these are more or less luxury foods.

After a few weeks, some effect should be noticed. But if this is negligible, cut down on bread and butter, omit sugar from your tea and don't eat any fried food.

This should ensure some noticeable reduction of bodyweight.

For weight gaining, eat as much as possible, especially eggs, cheese, butter, poultry, meat and sugar. But bear in mind the need for a balanced diet.

Take second helpings if you feel you can manage it without undue distress. Rest after each meal. Get plenty of sleep, relaxation, rest, whenever possible, lying down. Drink plenty of milk. Glucose drinks are helpful, too.

CHAPTER FIVE

Home or club training?

MOST people who start body building do so because of their underdeveloped physical condition and for many, this brings a problem. These are the people who hesitate to join a body-building club because they are extremely self-conscious about their physical appearance and do not relish the idea of stripping off in front of others. This is a natural and easily-understandable problem. But it should not be allowed to deter anyone from starting on a programme of body building.

Although I believe quicker and better progress can be made by training at a club, where one can get instruction from more experienced members and often inspiration from others who have well-developed bodies, there is no reason at all why shy and self-conscious people shouldn't train in the privacy of their own homes. Indeed, for many it might well prove to be the best thing to do – at least in the first months of training.

A beginner's schedule of exercises usually comprises simple and uncomplicated movements that require a minimum of technical skill to execute – unlike competitive weight lifting, with its movements requiring supervision by a competent instructor. Body-building movements, too, generally can be performed with less risk and in a smaller space than weight lifting. But many people train at home in private simply because they prefer to do it that way, having an inherent dislike of clubs and associations. Indeed, I would say that there are more people training with weights outside of clubs than there are inside.

The dangers of training by yourself are:

(*a*) you can easily practise the movements in a casual sort of way that doesn't bring maximum benefit. In a club, under instruction, this can be avoided.

(*b*) over-ambitious trainees might struggle with too-heavy weights in a manner that can be risky – or even use too-light weights that can be largely a waste of time.

(*c*) training sessions can be missed altogether if you aren't perhaps feeling up to par, or even just lazy.

When you belong to a club, there is a feeling of responsibility that often compels you to attend. This is an important point, because even if you sometimes don't feel like training once you have got to the club and started, the listless or tired feeling usually goes.

Another advantage of club training is that you don't have to purchase equipment. At a club it is there for you to use. All you pay is your club fees – generally on a very modest scale.

It all boils down to a matter of individual choice. My advice is: join a club if you possibly can. If you live in an area where there is no nearby club, then you may have to train at home. If you do, then consider the possibility of teaming up with one or two partners. The expenses of buying equipment can be shared and you will at least have some of the advantages of club training – companionship, shared interests and maybe some inspiration from a more-advanced partner.

Essential Equipment

One valuable asset of weight-lighting and body-building equipment is that it virtually never wears out – it will last you a lifetime.

It is best to obtain as much weight as you can afford, as once you have started body building and made some progress, poundages of up to 300lb. or more will soon be handled in some of the heavier movements, even by an average body-builder.

I would say that an absolute minimum for effective results is 150 lb. of discs, together with a bar-bell and two dumb-bell rods, a pair of squat stands and a bench. Iron boots for leg work are useful, too, although not entirely essential.

Preferably the bar-bell should be a minimum of 5 ft. in length and it is better if it can be fitted with a revolving sleeve. Four collars will be needed for your bar-bell.

The dumb-bell rods should be a minimum of 1 ft., with a centre sleeve and two collars on each.

Discs range from $1\frac{1}{4}$ lb. up to 50 lb., thus: $1\frac{1}{4}$, $2\frac{1}{2}$, 5, 10, 15, 25 and 50 lb.

Generally, sets can be bought in ranges of 90 lb., 120 lb., 150 lb. and so on, with a varied assortment of discs. But additional discs can be bought separately from time to time to add to your total weight.

Squat stands are a MUST, especially for home training, as they enable the Squat to be practised in safety and without the need to employ two assistants to help in placing the bar-bell on the shoulders.

A bench for pressing is important, too, as this movement is used in most schedules. If it is possible to obtain a bench with fitted stands, so much the better, as the weight can then be handled without requiring the assistance of anyone else.

A small wooden platform is useful and will save any possible damage to lino, carpets or floorboards. For general training, a size of about 7 ft. square will be sufficient, although if space and cash permit, a larger one is better.

It is essential to keep warm when training – and a track suit is best for this purpose when the temperature demands. If you can work stripped, with just a pair of trunks and sports boots or shoes, it is preferable for freedom of movement, but don't neglect keeping warm just for this purpose.

CHAPTER SIX

Schedules for the beginner

ALTHOUGH, as I have explained in an earlier chapter, the best progress can be made by training according to one's physical type, a complete beginner cannot do better than spend his first months of training on a schedule of standard exercises with standard repetitions – chosen for their simplicity of performance and proved effectiveness.

Later, when the muscular system is toned and strengthened and used to handling weights in various positions, graduation can be made to advanced exercises and type training, with its variation of repetitions and poundages.

If these standard exercises are assiduously followed and combined with good eating habits, plenty of sound sleep and fresh air, the muscles will show development in a reasonably short time, bodyweight will be increased, and a feeling of well-being will be experienced.

Preferably, it is best to train three or four times weekly for the best results, although gains can be made with only two weekly sessions. Once-a-week training is hardly sufficient to make any worthwhile progress.

Training should be in the evening, not earlier than two hours after a meal. But this may have to be adjusted according to one's domestic circumstances.

It may be found – in fact, it is almost always the case – that the first session or two will produce stiffness and soreness in the muscles. Don't worry about this. It is quite normal, and once the rhythm of training is in full swing you won't be troubled by such feelings.

Warming Up

Warming up is important before going on to your weight-training routine, and I recommend a few minutes of bending, stretching, free squats, running on the spot, or even a couple of minutes of skipping to get the blood flowing freely.

Particularly does this apply when the weather is very cold. There is nothing easier than painfully to pull or stretch a muscle by going straight on to lifting movements when the muscles haven't been warmed up.

Curve of Effort

Physiologically it is wise to start your routine with movements that do not call on the larger and main muscle groups to function. Then move on to the more strenuous part of the work involving the larger muscle groups and finally tapering off as one began.

The exercises have been planned to follow this principle, so perform them in the order given.

Poundages

I cannot give any definite poundages for the various exercises, as this depends entirely on the strength of each individual, but a trial on the following lines at the beginning will serve as a reliable guide.

First, try an approximate weight as suggested for each movement and see how many repetitions performed in strict style can be made. From this, it will then be fairly easy to ascertain the starting weight to be used.

Supposing 8 repetitions is the number to be used. If, in your trial, you can manage more than this, say 10 or 12, then the weight is too light. If less, say 5 or 6, then the weight is too heavy. Adjust accordingly and proceed from then on with this poundage.

Two Hands Curl (See Plate 1)

This is one of the most popular of arm exercises and develops the muscles on the front of the upper arm (brachialis and biceps).

Stand up close to the bar-bell, feet placed comfortably apart (about 15 inches). Squat down and grasp the bar-bell with an undergrip – that is, with the palms of the hands facing upwards. Make sure your grip is even, with each hand the same distance from each end of the bar-bell. Use a grip approximating shoulders' width.

Stand upright, with the bar-bell hanging on locked arms across the tops of the thighs. This is the actual starting position for the curling movement.

Now, flex the upper arms by curling the bar-bell upwards until it touches the top of the chest. As the bar-bell nears the chest, slightly tighten the grip and concentrate on a hard contraction of the muscles up the upper arms. The elbows should be taken forwards to facilitate the curling movement.

Pause for just a second, then lower the bar-bell to the starting position, completely relaxing the muscles.

Make sure that the arms are fully locked on return, pause a second, then make another repetition as before. Continue in this way until your number of repetitions are completed. Lower the bar-bell to the floor.

During this movement the body should remain upright – no swaying or leaning back to assist the curling movement. All the work must be done by power of the arms only.

Perform 8 repetitions. Rest for a few moments, then repeat 6 repetitions.

Suggested weight for average beginner of average body-weight – 55 lb. Adjust by trial method described above.

Press from Behind Neck (See Plate 2)

For muscles of the back of the arm (triceps) and the shoulders (deltoids). First clean the bar-bell to the shoulders as described in Chapter XVI for the Olympic Press. The grip should be about shoulders' width.

Now lift the bar-bell over the head to rest on the shoulders. This can be made easier by first dipping the legs a little, quickly re-straightening them and thrusting the bar-bell up towards the top of the head.

Your starting position for the press should now be with feet comfortably apart, trunk erect, bar-bell resting on shoulders.

Still maintaining the erect position, steadily and evenly press the bar-bell to arms' length overhead, making sure that you effect a full lock-out of the arms. Only the pressing muscles of the deltoids and triceps should be used, together with a tight bracing of the thighs and buttocks. No body sway or movement should be used to assist the press.

Perform 8 repetitions. Rest, then repeat 6 repetitions. Suggested weight – 70 lb.

Stiff-legged Dead Lift (See Plate 4)

For the muscles of the lower back – also increases mobility of trunk movement and stretches tight hamstrings at back of legs.

This movement is best performed standing on a strong box or something similar – about 6–12 in. high.

Starting position is body erect, feet either together or about 6 in. apart, bar-bell held with overgrasp – that is, knuckles forward – at about shoulders' width.

Making sure to keep the knees fully locked throughout the movement, bend forward from the waist to lower the bar-bell towards the floor as far as possible.

Most beginners will find they cannot reach their feet with the bar-bell and will probably feel a tightening of the hamstrings that tend to unlock the braced knees. But after a few sessions their ability in this movement will improve. Some, especially those with comparatively short legs, will eventually be able to lower the bar-bell lower than the top of the box.

When the maximum bent-over position has been reached, re-straighten to the erect position by using the lumbar muscles of the back.

On no account use the arms to assist in pulling up the weight. The arms must be kept straight throughout and act merely as links to hold the weight.

When the erect position has been reached lean back slightly from the waist to contract the lumbar muscles and lift up the chest. The head may be thrown back just a little to assist this movement.

This complete movement – the lowering and returning to the starting position – is one repetition.

Perform 10 repetitions. Rest, then repeat 8 repetitions. Suggested weight – 100 lb.

Squat (or Deep Knees Bend) (See Plate 3)

There are many variations of this most valuable exercise. But for this beginners' schedule use only the standard full Squat as described. Other variations will be covered later.

Using your squat stands, load the bar-bell to the required poundage. The stands should be such a height that you have to bend a few inches to get your shoulders under the bar-bell.

Make sure you get a centralized position, and hold the barbell with a grip slightly more than shoulders' width. Stand upright to lift the weight off the stands, and walk a pace or two backwards or forwards so that you are clear of the stands.

Position your feet comfortably apart, about 15–18 in., and you are ready to start the squatting movement.

Generally, I recommend that the feet be kept flat on the floor, but many beginners find it difficult to go into a full squat while keeping the feet flat. This is because either their hamstrings are tight or they have incomplete ankle flexion – or both. In this case, raise the heels just an inch or two by placing them on a suitable length of wood – or even each heel on a couple of discs. This will enable you to make the full squat more easily. But don't continue with this practice any longer than you can help. As soon as you are able, dispense with the wood or discs and perform flat-foot Squats.

The Squat should be made to the fullest extent that your mobility permits. Steadily lower the body, slightly resisting the weight so that you don't have literally to flop into the full knees-bend position.

The back must be kept as straight and as upright as possible in order to place the work on the legs. A rounded and bent-forward back means a mechanical position in which some of the work is transferred to the back in rising to the erect position. And there can be some risk of sacro-iliac strain when the spine is in this weakened position.

As soon as the lowest point is reached, immediately start to return to the erect position. At the beginning of the upward movement, make sure that the buttocks don't rise first as this will incline the trunk forwards. Endeavour to keep the buttocks down, the back as upright as possible (there will be some lean forward, of course, gradually coming nearer the upright position as the body rises) and the head up. This keeping up of the head assists in maintaining a good position.

Generally, I recommend breathing in as the effort is made in all exercises. This would mean, in the Squat, while rising to the erect position. But my own experience of this movement, and also the experience of others who have practised it much more than I have, indicates that the best breathing method is to inhale first before lowering into the squat, hold the breath for the short time it takes to descend, then start to exhale as the upward movement is made. Largely, it is a matter for each individual to adopt the method that comes most easily and is the most comfortable.

In between repetitions, I recommend that one deep breath be taken.

If there is any discomfort from the bar-bell resting on the shoulders, then by all means alleviate this by wrapping a towel or something similar around the bar-bell.

Perform 10 repetitions. Rest, then repeat 8 repetitions. Rest again, then repeat 6 repetitions. Suggested weight – 110 lb.

Straight Arm Pull-Over (See Plate 5)

For increasing mobility of the rib box, and an excellent chest expander.

This movement can be performed either while lying on the floor, or on a bench. If using the latter, a greater stretch can be made by allowing the bar-bell to be lowered below the line of the body. The shoulders should be in line with the end of the bench, allowing only the head to protrude over the edge.

Lie on the floor or bench with bar-bell held vertically at arms' length. From this starting position, steadily lower bar-bell backwards, making sure that the arms are kept straight throughout. Breathing is important and should be very deep. The action of the lowering of the bar-bell will uplift the chest and this should be accentuated by voluntary expansion, drawing in as much air as possible.

Don't pause when the bar-bell has been lowered to the fullest extent, but immediately return to your starting position. Exhale during this return movement.

Perform 12 repetitions. Rest, then repeat 10 repetitions. Suggested weight – 50 lb.

Bent-over Rowing Motion (See Plate 9)

For latissimus dorsi and trapezius muscles. The exercise also has some effect on the upper arms.

Your starting position is with the feet comfortably astride, body bent forwards so that it is in a line parallel with the floor, bar-bell grasped with a fairly-wide grip, knuckles uppermost.

It is essential that the body be kept stationary throughout the movement. As an aid to this, the head can be rested on a suitably-sized table or something similar, using a rolled-up towel for comfort.

The bar-bell should be suspended on locked arms. From this starting position, pull the bar-bell upwards until it touches the upper chest, at the same time forcing the elbows outwards and upwards.

Many trainees will find they cannot touch the chest with the bar-bell, but have to stop a few inches short. This is due to lack of full mobility in the upper back and shoulder regions, but perseverance will, in time, enable such people to reach the maximum pull to touch the chest.

When the bar-bell reaches the chest, hold it there for one second, then lower to starting position. Relax the muscles during this lowering movement, allowing the weight to drop with just a little resistance.

Hold a second in the starting position, then repeat until you complete the desired number of repetitions.

Perform 8 repetitions. Rest, then repeat 6 repetitions. Suggested weight – 80 lb.

Bench Press (*See Plates 6 and 7*)

One of the most popular and effective of all body-building movements and a great developer of the pectoral muscles of the chest, the anterior (front) deltoids and triceps.

You need a flat, level bench about four feet long, a foot or so wide and twenty or so inches high. If assistants (even one will do) are available, get them (or him) to hand you the bar-bell after you have adopted your position on the bench. This should be with your head resting on the end of the bench and your feet placed flat on the floor, comfortably apart.

Varying effects on the muscles can be obtained by using different widths of handgrip, but for a beginner it is best to get thoroughly used to the movement by keeping to the same grip for the first few weeks of training.

This width should be with hands spaced about 2 ft. apart – that is, between the insides of the hands.

Start by holding the bar-bell at arms' length after receiving it from your assistants. Incidentally, if no assistants are available, and your bench is not fitted with stands, you can still perform the exercise by first cleaning the weight to the shoulders, sitting down on the bench, then steadily leaning backwards until you are lying on the bench. But practise this movement first with a light weight.

Make sure you are firm on the bench and that the bar-bell is gripped evenly, so that it is well balanced.

Lower steadily until the bar-bell touches the chest a few inches below the line of the nipples. Hold for a second, then vigorously, but steadily and evenly, press back to arms' length.

During this pressing movement, ensure that there is no body movement at all – no raising of the buttocks from the bench or movement of the feet. Only the arms should move.

Make sure to lock the arms fully at the completion of the press. Hold for a second, then continue to complete the desired number of repetitions. Inhale as you press, exhale as you lower the bar-bell to the chest.

Perform 8 repetitions. Rest, then repeat 6 repetitions. Suggested weight – 100 lb.

Rise on Toes (See Plate 8)

For the calf muscles. The calves are probably the most difficult muscles to develop and for those who are not naturally endowed with full, rounded muscles, regular and persistent exercise over a long period will be necessary to bring out full development. A wide variety of exercises must eventually be used, but this is the standard movement generally used by beginners.

In order to obtain full-range ankle flexion, this exercise must be performed with the toes resting on the edge of a block of wood or something similar. This will allow the heels to drop below the level of the toes, a movement which flexes the tibialus anticus muscles on the front of the lower legs. At the other extreme of ankle flexion, with the heels raised as high as possible, the gastrocnemius, at the rear of the lower leg, is flexed.

Rest a bar-bell behind the shoulders as in the Squat exercise, stand so that about three or four inches of the foot covers the block. The feet should be placed comfortably apart, with the toes pointing straight forwards.

Rise as high as possible on the toes, hold a second or two, then lower the heels as far as possible.

At first, it may be difficult to balance on the block, but practice will soon rectify this.

High repetitions are of prime importance, perhaps more so than the amount of weight used, although it is wise to use as much weight as one can manage.

Perform at least 20 repetitions. Rest, then repeat another 20 repetitions. Suggested weight – 100 lb.

* * *

Finish off your weight-training schedule with a few abdominal exercises. Care of the abdominals is a major factor in cultivating and maintaining good health and a nice midriff appearance. Many of the best exercises of this nature can be performed without weights or apparatus.

One of the best is the overhead roll. Lie on the floor or a bench. Keeping the legs straight with toes pointed, bring them up and over the head as far back as possible, touching the floor behind your head if you can, or if on a bench, to the equivalent position. Return to the starting position, then carry on for 10 repetitions. Rest for a few moments, then repeat for another 8 repetitions.

Another effective movement is the 'jack-knife'. Lie on the floor. Then, keeping the legs straight, raise them upwards, simultaneously lifting the upper body to bring your head towards your legs as near as possible. Maintain your balance – you will probably find this difficult at first – by pressing with your hands on the floor just in front of the buttocks. Hold for a second or two, then relax and return to floor. Perform 8 repetitions. Rest, then repeat for another 6 repetitions.

The 'cat stretch' is one of the finest of free movements. It has some effect on the abdominals, but is mainly for the lower back muscles.

Start in the position of 'hands down' as for ordinary press-ups – hands placed on the floor shoulders' width apart, feet spaced apart the same distance. Now raise the buttocks and draw back the head and shoulders towards the feet until you resemble an inverted V. The arms will be in line with the head and trunk.

From this position, lower the hips towards the floor, at the same time lifting up the head and chest so that the back is hollowed as much as possible with the hips almost touching the floor. Ensure that your arms and legs remain straight throughout.

Making the movement rhythmical, go from one position to the other without pause for 10 repetitions. Rest a few moments, then repeat another 8 repetitions.

*   *   *

Your weight-training schedule should be made progressive by increasing the weights used every few sessions. Don't add too much weight—2½ or 5 lb. at a time is generally quite enough.

There is no need to force yourself too much in these early stages. Take it steadily, with gradual increases from time to time, and results will come. Keep your repetitions and sets the same – although if you feel like it, and have the time, you can perform an additional set of repetitions on one or more of the exercises now and again.

CHAPTER SEVEN

Advanced and specialized schedules

AFTER a few months' work on the beginner's schedule, most trainees will notice appreciable gains, both in well-being and muscular development.

The progress made will depend on several factors: (a) physical condition at the start, (b) natural potential, (c) physical type, (d) the amount of work done, and (e) the influence of other relevant factors, such as a proper intake of nourishing foods, a full amount of sleep and other aspects of good, clean living.

If one were to continue with these standard exercises – which comprise an efficient, although not by any means complete, body-building schedule – further progress would be made, and in most cases a good physique built, but in order to realize one's potential fully, graduation must be made to advanced and specialized work.

Special attention must be given to those parts of the body that are underdeveloped in order to build as harmonious a physique as possible, and exercises must be practised that work several muscle groups together – co-ordinated movements that develop qualities other than mere size.

The first few months of training enable one to get accustomed to handling weight in a fairly-comprehensive routine of varied movement. The muscular system is toned and strengthened, the internal organs begin to work more efficiently and general health is improved. Now, after this preliminary period, it is time to take stock of oneself.

Determine, as best you can, your physical type from the information given in Chapter Two, and from anyone who has some experience in this branch of physical culture. Then, follow the advice given regarding the number of repetitions and amount of resistance, remembering that, for *every* physical type, some exercises need more repetitions than others. The calves, for example, should always be worked with higher repetitions than other muscle groups.

The next stage is to determine the parts of the body that need special attention. In many it is the calves, in some the neck, in others the arms, and so on.

With this knowledge, your future training plans can take shape.

First, there should be an introduction of slightly more difficult exercises. Your beginner's schedule comprises simple, straightforward movements that should present no difficulty to anyone. All the exercises are performed with a bar-bell. There is nothing complicated about them ; nothing that requires any special concentration, balance or co-ordination.

Now, you can move on to exercises that work several muscle groups together, exercises with dumb-bells and co-ordinated movements requiring some degree of balance, timing and speed.

All the movements in the beginner's schedule are static and sectional. But in order to achieve greater co-ordinated muscular efficiency and mobility it is essential to include movements that demand greater bodily action and involve several major muscle groups.

Examples of such movements are the two Olympic lifts, the Snatch, and Clean and Jerk, and variations of these movements. There is no need to discard all the exercises in the beginner's schedule. Many of them can be retained. In fact, all of them can still be used from time to time for any special purpose, interwoven with others of a more active nature.

The time to start on an advanced schedule will vary with the individual. I suggest a minimum period of three months on the beginner's schedule. Some will be wise to extend this time, according to the progress made, for a further period of from two to four months. Any period longer than this shouldn't be necessary for the great majority. And in any case, after six months or so it is advisable to seek a change of movements to avoid any possibility of staleness or boredom.

Here is a typical schedule for advanced training, which can be used after your first few months of body building.

Warm up first, as usual, with freestanding movements – bending, stretching, squats, etc.

Swing Between Legs

For this movement you will need a swing-bell – a dumb-bell with discs loaded in the middle, leaving the ends free to be grasped with each hand. A 12-in. rod is sufficiently long.

Stand feet astride, wide enough to allow the dumb-bell to be placed between the legs, grasping each end, knuckles forward, in a squatting position, back flat, arms locked.

To start the movement, vigorously straighten the legs, at the same time swinging the bell forwards and upwards (on straight arms) until it is at arms' length overhead. You will then be in an upstretched position, trunk upright, knees braced and looking straight ahead. The bell should be taken back behind the head a little if shoulder mobility permits, with the back slightly hollowed.

Without pausing in this position, return to starting position by retracing the path of the upwards swing, squatting down by knees bending. But do not replace the bell on the floor. Instead, allow it to swing back between the legs as far as possible as you are in the low squat position.

As soon as you have reached the farthest backwards swing, bring the bell forwards again into another upwards swing.

This should be a rhythmical movement, fully working the thighs and small of the back, as well as stretching and uplifting the chest.

Essential points to watch are:

(*a*) keep back as flat as possible throughout; (*b*) keep arms locked throughout, and (*c*) breathe in rhythm with the movement, inhaling as the bell is raised overhead, exhaling as it returns between legs.

Perform 10 repetitions. Rest, then repeat 8 repetitions.

Alternate Press (See Plate 10)

Two evenly-loaded dumb-bells are needed for this variation of the standard pressing movement.

Stand feet astride, comfortably, with a dumb-bell placed at each side of the feet, with the rods pointing forwards.

Squat down to grasp the dumb-bells, then clean them to the shoulders. Stand erect, knees braced, with the bells held close to the front and side of the deltoids, the rods approximately at the height of the throat.

This is the starting position for the pressing movement.

First, press one dumb-bell directly overhead to locked arm, keeping the shoulders level. Lower to shoulder and at the same time press the other dumb-bell overhead so that they pass each other in the midway position. Continue this alternate pressing – one up, one down – until the desired number of repetitions is completed. Perform 5 Presses with each arm. Rest, then repeat 4 repetitions with each arm.

Front Squat (See Plate 11)

Similar to the Squat described in the beginner's schedule, but performed with the bar-bell held in front at the shoulders. Place the feet comfortably apart, clean the bar-bell to the shoulders, keep the elbows well forward, then lower the body into the full squat position.

Perform 10 repetitions. Rest, then repeat 8 repetitions.

Lateral Raise Lying (See Plate 15)

For the large pectoral muscles of the chest and the anterior deltoids.

Use two evenly-loaded dumb-bells. Lie comfortably on a bench, feet resting on the floor. Start by holding the bells overhead on locked arms, with knuckles outwards.

Steadily lower sideways, maintaining locked arms, until the arms are parallel with the floor, or even a little lower, at the same time inhaling deeply. Without pause, return to the starting position, exhaling.

Perform 8 repetitions. Rest, then repeat 6 repetitions.

Bend Over (See Plate 14)

Excellent for the lower back muscles. Also stretches tight hamstrings in the thighs.

Place bar-bell behind neck, resting on shoulders, feet placed comfortably apart. Maintain locked legs and steadily bend forward from the waist until the upper body is parallel with the floor. The buttocks will have to be taken back a little to counterbalance the forward disposition of the weight.

Inhale before starting the movement, then exhale while bending the body, inhaling as you return to the starting position.

Perform 8 repetitions. Rest, then repeat 6 repetitions.

Straddle Lift

Place the feet about 18 in. apart astride a bar-bell, grasping this with one hand in front of the thighs and one to the rear.

Keep the back flat and lift the bar-bell from the floor with leg power until the legs are fully locked. Lower almost to the floor again, then straighten up. This is a variation of the ordinary squat movement.

Perform 12 repetitions. Rest, then repeat 10 repetitions.

Inclined Bench Press

Similar to the ordinary Bench Press described in the beginner's schedule, but using an inclined bench. This has a different effect on the pectorals, concentrating more on the upper part of the large chest muscles.

If you have a bench in which the angle can be adjusted you can vary the angles to give different developing effects on the muscles involved.

Use the same repetitions and sets as recommended previously for the Bench Press.

Power Clean and Jerk

A good all-round movement for the upper body and building co-ordination and rugged power. See Chapter Twenty-three for description.

Perform 3 cleans, then 3 jerks from the shoulder. Rest, then repeat the same number. Rest, then repeat the same number.

Single-arm Rowing Motion

A similar movement to the Rowing Motion described in the beginner's schedule, but performed with a dumb-bell, employing each arm alternately.

Bend over until body is almost parallel with the floor and support yourself with one hand grasping a chair or table, holding a dumb-bell in the other hand, hanging down at arms' length.

Keeping body still, pull up dumb-bell to the upper chest, hold a second, then lower and repeat.

Perform 8 repetitions. Rest, then repeat 6 repetitions. Then perform with the other arm.

Wrestlers' Bridge Press

This is an excellent movement for the development of a firm, strong neck, which is an essential part of a good physique.

Place a cushion just in front of a loaded bar-bell. Stand in front of the cushion, with your back to the bar-bell. Place the top of the head on the cushion and lift the body so that only the feet are on the floor, assuming the well-known wrestlers' bridge position.

Put the hands behind the head to grasp the bar-bell with a shoulders'-width grip, then pull the bar-bell off the floor towards the chest, just clearing the face. Rest the bar-bell on the upper chest, then press upwards to arms' length above the face, similar to the press on bench. Lower to chest again and repeat.

Use only a light weight at first, until you are used to holding the head and neck in this unusual position. In fact, you would do well to practise holding the bridge position without any weights for a while, moving the head around for a minute or two, to accustom the neck muscles to the position.

Perform 6 repetitions. Rest a few moments, then repeat for 6 repetitions.

Side Bends

Stand erect, holding a dumb-bell in one hand at the side, feet comfortably astride.

Bend over to the side opposite to the dumb-bell, keeping the hips as level as possible, and making the movement from the waist. Bend directly to the side, not moving the body either forwards or backwards, with the bell moving up the thigh as the movement is made. Return to the starting position and repeat.

Perform 10 repetitions, holding the dumb-bell in the right hand, change over hands, and perform another 10 repetitions.

I haven't suggested any weights for the various exercises in this schedule. By now, you will have had some experience after following the beginner's schedule for several months and will be able to choose suitable weights accordingly.

Make the programme progressive, as before, by increasing

the weight used from time to time, but retaining the repetitions as suggested.

A variation is to make say, 8 repetitions, add some weight and perform 6 repetitions, add more weight and perform 5 repetitions, add more weight and perform 4 repetitions.

This is a popular system, but takes more time owing to the constant weight changing.

Occasionally, one can use heavier weights than usual and perform 5 or 6 sets with low repetitions of 4 or 5. In fact, there are many permutations of repetitions and sets that one can perform, and frequent variation does avoid any tendency to boredom or staleness, besides giving the muscles a change in the character of the schedule.

Bear in mind that high repetitions with light weights tend to build muscular size more than strength, low repetitions with heavy weights, strength more than size.

Other Exercises

Here are additional useful exercises for various body parts that can be incorporated into schedules from time to time. With a comprehensive list of exercises to choose from, schedules can be compiled to attain different objects. One may wish to specialize on the arms, for example, and several arm exercises can be welded into a schedule that contains at least one exercise for every body part. Never work on arm exercises alone to the exclusion of all others – similarly with other body parts.

Shoulder Shrugging

For the trapezius muscles. This exercise will improve the appearance of the shoulder and lower and back part of the neck.

Stand erect, holding a bar-bell at arms' length across the thighs. Keep the body still and the arms locked, then shrug the shoulders in a circular movement by first taking them back, then upwards, forwards, downwards, then back again to complete the circle.

Keep up the movement for 10 repetitions. Rest, then repeat 8 repetitions. Finally, repeat another 8 repetitions, circling the shoulders in the reverse way.

Bent-arm Pull Over (See Plate 12)

A variation of the Straight-arm Pull Over, performed as a short-range movement over the end of a bench. This exercise has a strong effect on the chest and triceps muscles.

Lie on a bench with the bar-bell held on the upper chest, using a narrow grip – hands about 8 in. apart. Take the bar-bell round the face in a semi-circular movement, while raising the elbows, until it is lowered below the head.

Keep the arms bent, which will prevent the bar-bell from being lowered too far.

Pull back close to face over the head to the starting position.

Perform 8 repetitions. Rest, then repeat 6 repetitions.

Snatch from the Hang

One of the best of all movements with weights – the Olympic lift described in Chapter Seventeen. This variation, repetition snatching without allowing the bar-bell to touch the floor, is a fine all-round movement, promoting stamina, co-ordination, balance and bodily power.

Make the first Snatch from the floor. Then, instead of re-placing the bar-bell on the floor, adopt a position in which the bar-bell is hanging at arms' length, lying across the thighs, while you are standing erect (commonly termed the 'hang' position).

Then lower the bar-bell *nearly* to the floor by a bending of the legs and lowering of the buttocks, keeping the back straight and upright as possible.

As soon as the bar-bell is near the floor, without any pause, retrace your path and vigorously pull the bar-bell into another repetition of the Snatch.

Perform 6 repetitions. Rest, then repeat 5 repetitions. Rest, then repeat 5 repetitions.

Lateral Raise Standing

For the lateral deltoids. Use two evenly-loaded dumb-bells and stand erect with bells held on locked arms at side, knuckles outwards. Raise arms out sideways, keeping them straight, until they are held at shoulders' level, or slightly above. Hold for a second or two, then lower to starting position.

Perform 8 repetitions. Rest, then repeat 6 repetitions.

One-arm Curl

A similar movement to the Two Hands Curl described in the beginner's schedule, but performed with one arm, using a dumb-bell. The movement is made more concentrated on the upper arm muscles by sitting down and leaning forward.

Start with the arm hanging down, grasping dumb-bell. Steadily curl the bell to the shoulder, fully contracting the upper-arm muscles. Hold the bell in the curled position for a few seconds, and try to contract the muscles even more. Then relax and return to starting position.

Perform 6 repetitions with each arm, Rest, then repeat 5 repetitions.

Bent-over Lateral Raise

To build full and rounded deltoids, this muscle group must be exercised from all angles. This variation of the lateral raise gets at the posterior (rear) and lateral (side) deltoids.

Start the movement by standing comfortably astride with the body bent forward parallel with the floor and arms hanging downwards, grasping two dumb-bells, knuckles outwards.

Keep the arms straight and raise them sideways until they are level with the shoulders. Hold for a second or two, then lower to starting position.

Perform 10 repetitions. Rest, then repeat 8 repetitions.

Seated Press With Dumb-bells (See Plate 13)

Another pressing movement having a strong effect on the deltoids and triceps. Press two dumb-bells together from the shoulders while in the seated position on a chair or bench. Make sure to lock the arms fully with each movement and to press the bells directly upwards. Position the feet to give a strong and safe position as there is a tendency to overbalance in this movement.

Perform 6 repetitions. Rest, then repeat 5 repetitions. Rest, then repeat 5 repetitions.

Thigh Extensions

Iron boots are the best appliances to use for this exercise. These are specially made boots to strap to the feet, but ordinary disc weights attached to the feet by leather straps will suffice.

Sit on a chair or bench so that the edge is level with the bottom of the thigh at the knee joint. With the iron boot or weight attached, raise the lower leg until the whole leg is extended and the muscles of the thigh fully tensed. Hold a few seconds, then relax to starting position. Exercise each leg in turn.

Perform 12 repetitions. Rest, then repeat 10 repetitions.

Hack Lift

Another effective thigh exercise, similar to the Squat, but with the bar-bell held behind the body or rested behind on a belt round the waist. Raise the heels on a wooden block or something similar. Lower into the squat position as low as possible and return.

Perform 15 repetitions. Rest, then perform 10 repetitions.

CHAPTER EIGHT

Questions and answers

I AM devoting this chapter to the discussion of typical problems of weight trainers, questions asked by those who in the main are beginners or those who perhaps train by themselves at home and remain out of touch with others of similar interests training at clubs where they can, generally, get more information and experience of training methods and other matters.

These questions and answers will serve the purpose of clarifying some of the material in other chapters and will cover many relevant points arising from the schedules and exercises I have described.

Question – After a few months of standard bar-bell exercises, I would now like to combine competitive weight lifting with training for a good physique.

Answer – To achieve maximum results from both weight lifting and physique building at the same time is usually difficult, as each sphere demands a different approach and methods of training ; and, as most of us have only a certain amount of time to spare for training, one sphere or the other will have to be neglected to some extent.

Much depends on your ambitions. If you are content to reach a reasonably high standard at both without necessarily being a champion, then the task is a little easier.

Weight lifters are generally the best-built of all athletes and the practice of competitive weight lifting only – combined with the many assistance movements that are used – will improve the physique, although not to the same extent as a specialized physique-building programme.

Perhaps the best programme for most people who have ambitions in both spheres is not to mix lifting and physique building at the same period and in the same schedule, but to devote specialized periods to each at different times.

For example, concentrate on competition work for a few months, perhaps in a period just prior to a championship you intend to enter, in order that all your training time available is devoted to the immediate object in view. When there is no competition in sight for some time, you can switch over to some specialized training for the weaker parts of the physique, returning to actual weight-lifting practice in time for the next competition. But in order to gain maximum benefit from this procedure, it would be wise to plan your schedules so that you have at least two months of good, solid work on one activity at a time. Switching to and fro every week or two, for example, will not bring such good results.

Question – I have been training with weights for about six months, starting with the main objective of gaining body-weight. I weighed 128 lb. at 5 ft. 8 in., with a small bone structure, but have since gained only 2 lb. despite training three times a week on twelve standard bar-bell exercises, using 12 to 15 repetitions in two sets on each exercise. I eat well enough, but often cannot sleep soundly. What do you advise?

Answer – Anatomically you appear to be the ectomorph type, who usually find it difficult to build a large musculature on their slender bone structure. Gains can be made, of course, and many of this type have shown excellent results, but generally the work is harder and gains slower to come than to those of more favourable physical types.

For maximum progress I advise using fewer exercises at a time, say six only, employing the largest muscle groups in such movements as the Squat (both back and front), Bent-over Rowing Motion, Press from Behind Neck, Power Clean and Jerk and Bench Press.

Use lower repetitions, from 5 to 8 (except in the Squat, when you can use up to 10) with correspondingly heavier poundages in sets of three. Your whole programme should last not longer than one hour, and if possible train four, or even five times a week.

But exercise is only part of the answer. Your food should always be of the best quality, including plenty of meat, fish, eggs, milk, milk and suet puddings, cheese and wholemeal bread.

A tranquil mind is essential to progress and if you are of the fretting and worrying type you must overcome this handicap. Relax the mind and body as much and as often as possible, particularly before retiring, as sound sleep is essential for your weight-gaining programme.

Question – What are the best exercises for developing the deltoids? I have a fair development elsewhere, but cannot get that full and rounded appearance on my shoulder muscles.

Answer – To get maximum development of the anterior, posterior and lateral deltoids, they must be given a wide variety of exercises.

Pressing overhead (in front and behind neck) ; bench pressing (using both wide and narrow grips) with bar-bell, and pressing with dumb-bells ; seated pressing with both bar-bell and dumb-bells ; lateral raises with dumb-bells (standing and in the bent-over position), crucifix with dumb-bells are all well-proved exercises.

Without weights, try handstand dips against the wall, and floor dips.

Question – I have been told that dumb-bells are better than a bar-bell for building strength and physique. Is this true?

In any case, I would like to add some dumb-bell work to my present bar-bell routine and would appreciate some information on the best dumb-bell exercises.

Answer – Whoever told you that dumb-bells are superior to a bar-bell certainly made a sweeping statement.

Admittedly, it is true that *some* dumb-bell exercises can bring better results than *some* bar-bell exercises – but the reverse is also true. And remember that dumb-bells are essential for certain movements (e.g. Lateral Raise, Alternate Press, etc.), while a bar-bell is essential for others (e.g. Squat, Dead Lift, etc.).

The answer is that for the best results, *both* dumb-bells and a bar-bell should be used.

The best dumb-bell exercises generally are those in which a similar movement cannot be performed with a bar-bell, such as the Lateral Raise Standing and Lying ; Crucifix ; Alternate Press, standing, seated and on bench ; One Hand Swing ; also swing between legs to arms' length overhead with swing-bell.

Question – I have been weight training for almost a year, with fairly good results. But now I find I cannot spare so much time for my workouts and would appreciate a brief schedule of the best body-building exercises.

Answer – A result-producing schedule can be run through in less than an hour, so if you can spare forty to fifty minutes on three days a week, try the following:

1. A few minutes' warming up with bending and stretching, etc.
2. Squat with light to moderate weight – 20 repetitions.
3. Press from Behind Neck – 8 repetitions, 2 sets.
4. Bent-over Rowing Motion – 8 repetitions, 2 sets.
5. Squat with heavy weight – 6 repetitions, 3 sets.
6. Press on Bench – 8 repetitions, 2 sets.
7. Squat (same weight as in 2) – 20 repetitions.

You will notice that the basis of this schedule is the Squat, one of the best of all exercises. This will build the legs and increase chest mobility and capacity. The remaining exercises are for the upper body.

It must be appreciated that such a brief schedule is by no means a fully-comprehensive body-building course, but for the special purpose required in this particular case it provides a fair all-round workout in the minimum of time.

Question – I wish to increase my chest measurement, which is only 36 in. at a height of 5 ft. 9 in. and bodyweight of 144 lb. What are the best exercises with weights?

Answer – Increasing the chest measurement and appearance isn't a particularly difficult task for any normal person, and gains of from 2 to 4 inches (and even more in time) can be expected if a sensible training schedule and living régime is adopted.

Increases are effected by (*a*) stretching the rib box and (*b*) building up the large surrounding muscle groups of the pectorals and latissimus dorsi.

One of the best rib-stretching movements is the Straight-arm Pull Over performed on a bench with a light to moderate weight in groups of high repetitions. Perform from 12 to 15 repetitions in 2 or 3 sets.

When this movement is combined with a special version of the Squat, performed alternately, i.e. one set of Squats followed by a set of Pull Overs and so on, maximum results will be obtained.

Although primarily a leg exercise, the Squat is very effective for chest building when used as follows:

Use just a light to moderate weight – a little less than body-weight for a beginner and a little more than bodyweight for the more advanced man – and take three or four deep breaths between each repetition. The number of repetitions should be between 15 and 20 for the best results, the object being to force deep breathing to encourage stretching of the rib box.

Any vigorous activity which forces involuntary deep breathing is good for rib-box expansion, and the Squat certainly comes in this category when performed as described.

Repetition snatching and cleaning are fine movements, too, for forced deep breathing.

Pectoral and latissimus dorsi development can be achieved by using such movements as the Bench Press on flat and inclined benches ; Lateral Raise lying on bench, also the variation known as the Flying exercise with bent arms ; and the Bent-over Rowing Motion. Again use light to moderate weights in sets of from 8 to 12 repetitions.

Exercises without weights can include floor dips and chinning the bar.

Question – I view with alarm my ever-increasing waistline. From a trim 29 in. a few years ago, when I was active in many sports, my waist now measures 34 in. Would weight training help? Or would free exercises be better?

Answer – One's physical type governs, to a large extent, the accumulation of fat and increased bodyweight as the years go by. This problem is much more prevalent and troublesome among the endomorph type (large boned, often short-to-medium height and with a large abdominal cavity). The ecto-morph (small-boned and leaner) and the mesomorph (in-between) types are not so prone to put on excess fat in the waist and hips area, and even if they do, find it easier to reduce when the effort is made.

The best method of reducing the waistline is a combination of suitable exercises and diet. But it should be remembered that as the condition has been gradually getting worse over a long period, then the work and effort required to reduce will have to be great and extended. Obviously the best way to control the waistline is to do sufficient work and to exist on a suitable diet so that any tendency to put on fat is checked.

All starchy, fat-forming and greasy foods should be curtailed, or even avoided, and plenty of fruit should be eaten. Liquid intake should also be reduced, particularly if one regularly drinks beer or stout.

Exercise should be of the vigorous type, including plenty of trunk twisting and bending movements. A wide variety of abdominal free movements should be practised, including legs raising from the supine position to touch the floor behind the head (overhead roll) ; legs raising combined with sitting up to form a V shape (jack-knife) ; jumping off the floor and extending legs upwards and sideways as much as possible ; sitting on floor with legs stretched out wide and trunk twisting to touch left foot with right hand and vice versa.

With a medicine ball, team up with a partner in distress and throw to each other rapidly, aiming to each side of the body alternately so that you have to keep on the stretch and twist to catch the ball and return.

Lifting movements with weights should include alternate bending from side to side holding a dumb-bell in each hand ; trunk twisting from side to side with bar-bell held behind neck ; alternate legs raising with light iron boots, or discs attached to feet.

All repetitions should be high and performed at a brisk tempo. Wear warm clothing so that you perspire freely.

During all waking hours cultivate the habit of keeping the stomach held in, whether sitting, standing or walking ; also always sit and stand as tall as possible.

Question – I have always admired broad shoulders in a man and am particularly anxious to broaden my own. I have done a little weight training and possess both bar-bell and dumb-bells. Can you tell me the best means of training?

Answer – It isn't possible to alter the bone structure of your shoulders if you are fully grown. The only way to broaden your shoulders is to develop the deltoids, particularly the lateral section of this muscle group.

Try the Lateral Raise Standing, raising the dumb-bells from the hang position at the sides to a position where the arms are slightly above parallel with the floor. Lower and repeat. Also try the Crucifix, lowering the dumb-bells from arms' length overhead to a point where the arms are parallel with the floor. Raise upwards again and repeat.

Wide-arm pressing with bar-bell is also good. Use repetitions from 5 to 8 in these movements with as much weight as you can handle in correct form. Perform a few sets of each exercise.

Without weights, try wide-arm chinning the bar – using sets of from 7 to 10 repetitions.

Question – Owing to various commitments and other circumstances I must do my weight training at home and can work only in a very confined space in my bedroom. This means that there is little space for using a bar-bell. However, I have two dumb-bells and would appreciate a good all-round schedule. I have up to 200 lb. in weight available.

Answer – Actually it is possible to use a short bar-bell in the same space as you would use for dumb-bells. However, here is a suitable dumb-bell schedule which should be practised on alternate days if you can spare that time.

One of the disadvantages of using dumb-bells is the extra weight changing involved – discs can be floated on a bar-bell without continually unlocking the collars, whereas they must always be locked on dumb-bells; and there are also four collars to contend with. Consequently it is often advisable to use exercises that entail the minimum amount of weight changing – unless one is prepared to go to the extra trouble.

These exercises are grouped in three categories of weight – light, medium and heavy. I don't know your capabilities or strength, so suggest three weights of 10 lb. on each bell, 30 lb. and 60 lb. Adjustments can be made as necessary by trial and error.

Warm up first with a few minutes of stretching, bending, free squats, etc. Then start off with the 10-lb. dumb-bells on the following exercises:

Alternate Arms Raising forwards from hang position at sides to arm's stretch overhead, with the dumb-bells passing each other at shoulders' level. Three sets of 6 repetitions each hand.

Lateral Raise Standing. Three sets of 8 repetitions.

Crucifix (lower dumb-bells from overhead to shoulders' level and return overhead). Three sets of 6 repetitions.

Lying on back, legs raising to perpendicular with one dumb-bell held between feet. Three sets of 8 repetitions.

Now load dumb-bells to 30 lb. each for the following:

Alternate Press. Two sets of 8 repetitions.

Bent-over Rowing Motion. Two sets of 8 repetitions.

With the 60-lb. dumb-bells perform the following:

Deep Knees Bend, holding dumb-bells at the shoulders. Three sets of 8 repetitions.

Press on Bench. Three sets of 8 repetitions.

Stiff-legged Dead Lift, standing on blocks of wood or a box. Three sets of 8 repetitions.

Make the schedule progressive by adding slightly to the weights every few workouts.

CHAPTER NINE

Weight training
(i) for boys

ALTHOUGH the best results from weight training can be obtained by starting at an early age, I don't think it is wise to start *too* young. A lot will depend on the boy. Anyone who matures early and is perhaps above average in height and weight can start weight training at an earlier age than is normal.

My own view is that from about the age of ten or eleven a boy should indulge for a few years in normal sporting activities such as football, baseball, swimming, cycling, running, etc.

This activity will develop qualities of stamina, mobility, co-ordination, balance, etc., by the time a boy has reached the middle teens, he can think of specializing at one particular activity at which he seems naturally gifted or which he particularly enjoys.

Many boys, of course, are quite content to dabble in various activities and show no desire to specialize. Perhaps for most youngsters this is the best outlook and often one which brings the greatest enjoyment. But for a boy ambitious enough to want really to excel at any particular sport or game, or who shows a special aptitude and potential, specialization is essential because in these days of fierce competition, only the dedicated specialist can hope to reach the top.

Many young boys will show an interest in building a good physique. Others may wish to develop extra strength to help them at their chosen sport.

One important point has to be watched when youngsters start body building. Their youthful enthusiasm often tends to make them over ambitious and they want to progress too fast.

I am no believer in rushing things for the very young, so they must be watched carefully, with their programmes scheduled to carry them along at a steady, controlled pace. Poundages used must be on the light side and any attempt on their part to pile on the weight too much and too often must be curbed.

The principles of progression must be followed, but at a reasonable and sane rate. Proper instruction must be given in the methods of performing the various movements.

With these provisos I have nothing against weight training for the young teenager and indeed recommend it as a very fine outlet for his physical ambitions.

(ii) for the older man

The old idea of being 'too old at forty' has largely died out. Nevertheless, there is still a school of thought that believes exercise, games and sports are strictly for the youngsters, and that any form of physical activity for those approaching middle age is unnecessary and perhaps even dangerous. Actually it is just as necessary to exercise at forty as it is at fourteen. Just as necessary at sixty as at sixteen.

Exercise in some form is essential throughout life if one wants complete fitness. But naturally it must differ in its nature at various ages.

From a body-building point of view, the most active and result-producing period is probably between the ages of sixteen and thirty. But this is only a broad average. Many people don't start body building until they are in their late teens or during their twenties. Some start even later.

Then there is the question of how long one should continue body building – at whatever age one starts.

If a start has been made at the average age of sixteen or seventeen, then maximum development has generally been reached at about twenty-five or thirty, depending on what effort one has put into it. But there is no reason why one should stop exercising, even if no further progress can be made in muscular gains. Good health is far more important, and continued exercise, combined with good food and living habits, is an important factor in maintaining robust health throughout life.

For one who starts at a later age, maybe in the late twenties or even the thirties, the same results cannot reasonably be expected. Nevertheless, I know of literally hundreds of instances where excellent progress has been made by older people.

It is never *too* late to start. But the later it is, the more care one must take. An older man who has led a life of comparative idleness and then suddenly decides to start body building cannot expect to plunge into this with the same intensity and enthusiasm of a younger man, nor can he expect to achieve the same results. Muscles that have been dormant for many years will rebel when suddenly called on to be active in a vigorous way.

So older men who start out on a body-building programme must proceed with due caution.

First, perhaps, a period of a few weeks on freestanding exercises, then a body-building schedule with very light weights, combined with some specialized work on the abdominals, which most likely will have been neglected.

Progress can be made in the normal way, adding to the weights used as strength is gained – although this progress need not be forced quite so much as in the case of the younger man.

Most older men who do decide to practise weight training will probably be more interested in building a reasonable physique and in improving their general health rather than in concentrating on building maximum development.

Workouts should be of a fairly short duration – say 45 minutes to an hour – using six or seven exercises of an all-round nature.

Special attention should be given to the abdominals and the legs. The abdominals, because a firm and trim mid-section is one of the main essentials to good health ; and the legs, because vigorous activity of these vital body parts keep one nimble – which is an increasing necessity as the years pass. Also, leg activity in the way of the various forms of Squats is valuable in giving greater efficiency to the vital heart and lungs.

It will be reassuring to the older man to know that medical opinion is becoming more and more on the side of exercise. Doctors are calling exercise good medicine – good for the heart and good for a long life.

Dr. Paul D. White, one of the world's leading heart specialists, says: 'The general warning to stop vigorous exercise at forty seems to me to be ridiculous and more likely than not, actually to lead to an increase of coronary arteriosclerosis.

'It is true enough that heart disease is now the leading killer of Americans. But heart experts find that half the heart attacks come during sleep and only about 2 per cent happen during severe exertion. These are the cases that get publicity and blame sports of causing heart attacks.'

'One of the biggest mistaken notions', Dr. Klumpp, another medical expert, says: 'is that heart attacks are due to hard work, excesses, over exercise and the tempo of modern living. On all sides we are bombarded with the advice "take it easy, don't work so hard, slow down. Do you want to kill yourself? Remember, you're not as young as you used to be." '

'It is mostly too much and not enough exercise that contributes heavily to heart attacks. Any slackening of activity leads very quickly to atrophy or degeneration. The atrophy of disuse, both mental and physical, is the most insidious and, in my opinion, the most deadly disease known to man. We don't wear out, we rust out.'

PART II

WEIGHT TRAINING FOR ATHLETES

CHAPTER TEN

A stronger athlete is a better athlete

THE use of weights for improving one's ability at various sports and games is now largely accepted by the world's leading coaches. It wasn't always so. Until only a few years ago there was a marked refusal to recognize the value of resistance exercises for this purpose, the opinion being held that this type of training tended to develop slowness of movement and muscle binding (whatever that is!).

Many of the old-timers in weight training have advocated for years that, other things being equal, the stronger athlete would win, or would shine most in games. They did not claim that weight training would improve basic skill, but that it would enable this skill to be used in a more efficient manner. But these views were violently opposed by the coaches and other authorities, and indeed by most of the participants themselves.

Now the breakthrough has been made and there is no doubt at all that this is the age of the weight-trained athlete and sportsman. Almost daily one can read in the national and local Press some reference to sportsmen (and sportswomen, too) who augment their normal training with bar-bell and dumb-bell work. So at long last it seems that the barriers of prejudice have almost been swept away.

More than thirty years ago I became convinced of the benefits of weight training. Although my main interest leaned towards competitive weight lifting as a sport, I found that my other activities of football, hand balancing and swimming were materially helped by the regular use of weights. Sceptics there were then by the hundred, despite growing evidence to support the contentions of the few who were convinced that a stronger athlete was a better athlete. But the work of the pioneers in those early days has now borne fruit and while everyone is not yet convinced the number of disbelievers is dwindling, and I am sure that in the very near future the value of weight training will be finally and completely accepted by all.

Skill and technical perfection with only moderate strength just isn't enough these days when the standard of athletics and sporting achievement is so high. With the great advances in coaching, and the consequent development of many highly-skilled technicians, victory is often dependent on other factors and the man who has greater strength and durability to go with his skill more often than not comes off best.

We read plenty nowadays of famous football teams who have added weight training to their normal training. And the great benefit here is the insurance against injury. Stronger muscles greatly help to reduce the injury rate in this game where the performer has to manoeuvre, swerve, stop, suddenly change direction, etc., often on greasy and treacherous surfaces. A weight-trained footballer can stand up to the hazards much more easily than one who has never practised any form of resistance training.

In athletics and swimming, among other sports, many of the leading performers have reached the top with the aid of weights. Famous Jon Konrads, the former wonder-kid of Australian swimming, trained with weights twice weekly in addition to a strenuous swimming programme of several hours a day. Indeed, a large proportion of leading champions and top-liners in all sports use weights.

Many athletic clubs, big and small, have added weights to their equipment. Leading A.A.U. coaches, finally convinced of the value of weight training after initially being sceptics, now urge that all athletes should use weights.

In professional boxing, one outstanding example was former world champion Randy Turpin, whose regular use of weight training helped him to win a world title for Britain. And there are many, many more.

It should be appreciated that this form of training should be only a supplement to the normal training for a particular event, which should still form the greater part of one's training time.

But however well and diligently one trains there comes a time when the practice of an athlete's event ceases to give sufficient work to produce any gains in strength, so it becomes necessary to use specialized methods like weight training.

An athlete needs to be strong so that he can use his technique with greater skill and efficiency and weight-trained muscles have improved 'tone' and contractibility and will respond more readily to sudden exertion and all-out effort.

CHAPTER ELEVEN

The best exercises

FIRST, let me emphasize that this is by no means a complete treatise on weight training for athletes, which would need a whole book completely to cover the subject.

Space limitations permit me to give only general advice and a broad outline of the best exercises. Any athlete or sportsman who wishes to include this form of training in his schedules should practise the standard exercises I suggest as a basic schedule, plus a few more of a specialized nature related to his particular sport or event. With a knowledge of the particular requirements and the muscle groups involved, a selection can be made from the additional exercises that I list.

My suggested basic schedule is a selection of exercises from the beginner's schedule covered in Chapter Six. These are sufficient to build a fair degree of all-round development and strength (a condition that many sportsmen lack).

The addition of three or four specialized movements makes up a complete weight-training schedule that can be used as convenient by the athlete.

Many sports and games have a close season, and some athletes and sportsmen like to use this close season as a period devoted to weight training, when it can be used several times weekly without it clashing with their normal sporting activity.

Others prefer to use weight training regularly each week throughout the year, even during their active season. This means that it is difficult to devote, say, three sessions weekly to weight training, as obviously the bulk of one's training must be devoted to the sport or event. There is the point, too, that one might easily overtrain if trying to incorporate a full weight-training programme into one's athletic schedules.

Perhaps the best compromise is for one to practise weight training once a week during the active season, then step this up to three sessions weekly during the close season.

It is a matter for each individual to decide according to his inclination, his physical capacity for training and other circumstances.

Here is my suggested basic schedule:
Press from Behind Neck.
Stiff-legged Dead Lift.
Squat.
Straight-arm Pull Over.
Bench Press.

To complete, add three or four special exercises designed to strengthen the muscle groups that play the biggest part in the performance of the relevant event.

For example, a high or long jumper needs springy, explosive strength in the legs. He will get some benefit from the ordinary Squat, but a useful extra movement is the jumping Squat. A shot putter can use the power-jerk with dumb-bell. And so on.

Another aspect is the number of repetitions. Field athletes like the shot putter, discus and javelin thrower, the high and long jumper, need to use lower repetitions, with correspondingly heavier weights, than the runners, whose activity is far different.

The field athlete puts forth one concentrated, explosive effort, then relaxes for a time before repeating another single effort – exactly similar to the competitive weight lifter. So his weight training must be on similar lines to the weight lifter – generally, low repetitions, using heavy weights.

On the other hand, the runner has to maintain a long, sustained effort which demands, to a much higher degree, stamina. His weight training should involve higher repetitions, with lighter poundages.

Here is a list of some useful exercises additional to the standard ones previously listed.

Jumping Squat

Place the bar-bell behind the neck as for the ordinary Squat, with the feet held about 18 in. apart. Start the movement by first bending the knees to lower the body about six inches, then spring up in the air as high as possible. Land first on the toes, then allow the heels to touch the ground and lower the body into the regular squat position. Without pause, return to the upright position and straight into another jump. Continue in this manner until the desired number of repetitions is performed.

Do 1 set of 5 repetitions, then 2 sets of 3, 2 sets of 2, then three or four single movements, increasing the weight as the repetitions are lowered.

Useful for high and long jumpers in particular.

One Arm Power Jerk

Use a dumb-bell, holding it at the shoulder, with the feet spaced comfortably apart, free arm held out sideways to help maintain balance. Start by dipping the body a few inches, then quickly restraightening legs and thrusting the dumb-bell overhead. As the arm nears the locked position quickly lower the body again by bending the knees to facilitate the arm lock. Straighten the knees again to assume an erect position. Lower dumb-bell to shoulder and repeat.

In order to avoid too much weight changing when using a dumb-bell (it is easier with a bar-bell as the discs can be 'floated' on each end without unlocking collars) use a fixed poundage and perform 5 or 6 sets of 3 repetitions. Occasionally, use a heavier weight and use 7 or 8 sets of 2 repetitions.

Useful for the shot putter.

Alternate Splitting

A fine co-ordinated movement that will build leg strength and stamina. Useful for all sportsmen.

Hold a bar-bell at the shoulders in the clean position or placed behind the shoulders. Start with feet astride about 6 to 9 in., then simultaneously split both feet and move into the low split position as used in the Snatch, described in Chapter Seventeen, one leg forward, one backward.

Hold on for a second or two to ensure a good balance. Then raise the body a little by a slight straightening of the legs and quickly reverse the legs position by moving the front leg to the rear and the rear leg to the front, going into the low split position as before.

Reverse legs again and continue alternately until the desired number of repetitions is completed.

This is a strenuous exercise and will force one to breathe deeply and rapidly. Perform 3 sets of 8 repetitions (4 with each leg).

Punching with Dumb-bells

Use two fairly light dumb-bells. Start by holding them at the shoulders, leaning forward slightly. Punch one hand forward, as in the running action. Return to shoulder, at the same time punching forward with the other hand. Continue punching alternately, forwards and backwards, as if running.

Perform 2 sets of 10 repetitions with each arm.

Useful for sprinters to give greater strength and control to the arm action.

Fast Dead Lift

The Two Hands Dead Lift is a fine movement for building rugged bodily power and a strong grip, especially useful for heavy athletics such as hammer throwing and shot putting, also for footballers and wrestlers, where heavy bodily contact is frequently made.

See Chapter Twenty-three for description of movement, which in this instance should be performed at a fast tempo. This necessarily cuts down the weight one can use. However, using low repetitions it is possible to work up to reasonably heavy poundages.

Perform 6 sets of 3 repetitions, without replacing the bar-bell on the floor in between movements, but stopping the downward movement just before the bar-bell reaches the floor. Make sure that you keep the back as straight as possible throughout.

Stepping on Bench

Soccer players will benefit specially from this excellent leg and stamina movement, but it is good for all sportsmen.

Utilize a strong and firm bench. With a bar-bell placed behind the shoulders, place the right foot on the bench and step up with the left foot. Step off by placing the right foot on the floor, followed by the left foot to complete one repetition.

Then reverse the procedure, stepping up with the left foot this time. Continue in this alternate manner until the desired number of repetitions is completed.

Perform 12 repetitions (6 with each leg). Rest, then perform 10 repetitions.

Pinch Gripping

A strong grip and wrists are essential for many sports, including shot putters, pole vaulters and hammer throwers.

One of the best exercises is pinch gripping with weights. Stand two or three discs, held together, on end and lift them off the floor by gripping them with the fingertips. Hold for a few seconds before replacing. Progression can be made by using larger discs to get heavier weight and also by using just two or three fingers at a time – such as thumb and forefinger, thumb and little finger, etc.

Perform as many repetitions as necessary to give the fingers sufficient work and afterwards alternately grip and relax the fingers to ease off the tension.

Legs Raise with Iron Boots

Fix iron boots or discs to the feet and lie on back. Raise legs upwards, kept straight until they are at right angles to floor. Lower to floor and immediately return for another repetition.

It will be easier to concentrate the exercise on the legs and lower abdominals if the hands are held behind the head grasping a loaded bar-bell or some fixed object.

Useful for high jumpers, who require strong leg extensors and abdominals.

Perform 3 sets of 8 repetitions.

Chinning the Bar

Particularly useful for the pole vaulter, who has to haul himself upwards by pulling down on his pole.

This is a well-known exercise and requires little explanation. Use a variation of grip widths and both over and reverse grips in pulling up to chin level. Progress can be made by attaching weights to the body.

Perform 2 or 3 sets of 6 repetitions. When this becomes easy, add weight by attaching discs to the waist by using a belt and leather strap.

Alternate Press

Use two dumb-bells and perform as described in Chapter Seven. Useful for improving the power of the shoulder and arms' drive for sprinters.

Perform 3 sets of 8 repetitions (4 with each arm).

Lateral Raises

Use both the Lateral Raise Standing and Lying as described in Chapter Seven. Useful for discus throwers, as it develops the deltoids that are strongly employed in swinging the discus and holding the arm out sideways.

Perform 4 sets of 5 repetitions.

Sideways Swing

Stand with feet well astride, holding a dumb-bell in front of the chest, with the elbow extending sideways. From here, turn the body to the right (assuming using the right hand first) from hips, at the same time swinging the dumb-bell in a circular movement to the right and extending the arm so that the upper body is at right angles to the front with the arm pointing backwards from the front.

Without pause, return to the starting position and repeat.

Useful for the discus thrower. Perform 5 sets of 5 repetitions.

Trunk Turning

Stand feet astride with a bar-bell held across the back of the shoulders. Without moving the feet, twist the body round to the right as far as possible, then return and continue to twist the body round to the opposite side. Continue the twisting movement from one side to the other.

Perform 2 sets of 12 repetitions (6 to each side).

Useful for all activities in which body twists have to be made – hammer throwers, footballers, etc.

Repetition Snatching

Perform as described in Chapter Seven. Useful for all sportsmen, as this movement develops all-round power and agility and stamina.

Perform 3 sets of 6 repetitions.

Progression should be made by adding slightly to the weights used every few weeks, or when it is felt that one is capable of using heavier weights. Don't force the progress too much, as a weight lifter might, as the purpose of this form of training is not to build up strength to the same extent that a weight lifter requires. One will get stronger, of course, with continued use of a selection of the exercises, but this progress is not so vitally important as it is in the case of a competitive weight lifter.

PART III

WEIGHT LIFTING AS A COMPETITIVE SPORT

CHAPTER TWELVE

Modern Olympic weight lifting

MODERN competitive weight lifting is one sport of the strength athlete but to be a top-line or champion weight lifter one needs not to be only strong but also courageous, athletic, fast and mobile in joint and limb.

Many doctors and other professional men practise weight lifting both as a sport and a means of keeping fit and one of the Russian world and Olympic champions, Doctor Arkady Vorobyev, is an eminent surgeon. Another, Yuri Vlasov, the world's strongest Olympic lifter, is a man of outstanding intelligence and his favourite diversion is the study of philosophy. He writes expert commentaries on aviation-engineering as well as fiction and poetry.

The Japanese seven-man team for the 1960 Olympic Games was composed almost entirely of university students and graduates and in this country almost every university has a weight-lifting group and annual university championships are held.

It will be seen that there is much more to weight lifting than just being brawny enough to heave up a heavy weight with muscles bulging and eyes popping – which is the usual conception of the man in the street.

The sport has been a firmly established part of the Olympic Games since the modern revival of the four-yearly event in 1896. Going back to that year, we find that the weight lifting event was divided into two separate contests – a one-handed lift and a two-handed lift, both overhead movements in the Clean and Jerk style (incidentally, the two hands' contest was won by an Englishman, Launceston Elliott). It is interesting to note, too, that there were no bodyweight classes in those days – all entered irrespective of size or weight and modern Olympic lifting as we know it did not really begin until 1920. In that year the Games were held at Antwerp and the lifts were the

One Hand Snatch, One Hand Clean and Jerk and the Two Hands Clean and Jerk.

In Paris, in 1924, the Two Hands Clean and Press and the Two Hands Snatch were added, to make a five-lift championship.

These lifts were replaced later by the 'Olympic Three' – the Two Hands Clean and Press, the Two Hands Snatch and the Two Hands Clean and Jerk – which have remained the standard lifts to the present day.

Now, with more than seventy nations affiliated to the International Federation, weight lifting is practised on a vast worldwide scale.

There are, of course, many more movements than the 'Olympic Three' in use. In Britain, for example, the governing body recognizes no less than thirty-one different movements, although the present-day tendency is to concentrate on only a fraction of this number.

The three Olympic lifts were selected as being the best representative set, bearing in mind the need for a streamlined programme to satisfy the Games' organizers, and the popularity of these three lifts.

As a double-handed set, used for an Olympic sport, I believe they *are* the best, remembering that two of the movements – the Snatch and the Clean and Jerk – can be termed athletic in the true sense of the word – fast, co-ordinated movements that should be part and parcel of an Olympic performer.

The main features of present-day activity are the Olympic Games and the annual world's championships which are staged in between the Olympic events, but we have other major championships such as the Pan-American Games, Asian Games, European championships, etc., and the national championships of all countries practising the sport.

World competition is governed by the International Weight Lifting Federation, which currently has its headquarters in England. This body was formed in 1920 and is responsible for the arrangements for world championships, the Olympic Games weight-lifting and other major continental and international events. Its other main function is to develop and control weight lifting on an international scale. It has to co-ordinate and supervise the activities of the national federations that are directly affiliated to it, and to set up such regulations as may be found desirable and practicable from time to time. It is responsible for the registering of world records and for ensuring that the complete and proper regulations are carried out.

Managing the Federation is a committee made up of a president, six vice-presidents, a general secretary-treasurer, an assistant secretary and four members.

A Congress is held every four years during the Olympic Games, in the town where the competition takes place, and is attended by the delegates of the various affiliated nations. The congress considers proposals put forward by the nations, which are debated and then voted on in the normal constitutional manner.

From applications received, the Congress allocates the world championships which are held every year except Olympic Games year. It also allocates the European championships, when these are staged as a separate event if the world championships are held in a non-European country.

These world championships are indeed the high spot of each year's international activity and in most countries where they are held attract large and enthusiastic audiences. The post-war rivalry between the two outstanding nations, Russia and U.S.A. has largely contributed to this wide-spread interest and has been responsible to a great extent for the incredibly high standard of modern Olympic weight lifting.

Now, during the past few years, nations like Poland and Hungary are seriously challenging U.S.A. for second place to the Russians.

It is interesting to note the great differences of approach to the sport between the leading nations.

In the U.S.A., for many years the greatest weight-lifting nation, the A.A.U. (American Athletic Union) controls all amateur activities, with each of the various sports having its own governing committee.

With weight lifting only a minor sport, the grants allowed by the A.A.U. for participation in such events as world championships and international contests are small, and were it not for a man like wealthy Bob Hoffman, a super-enthusiast who regularly finances the trips of the U.S.A. national teams to all parts of the world, the standard of their champions would never have been so high.

Bob, together with the recent help of another grand worker and financial supporter, Clarence Johnson, who is the A.A.U. chairman for weight lifting and the President of the International Weight Lifting Federation, has played a major part in providing the American champions with the competition from other leading nations that has provided many stirring battles on the world championships platform.

Because of the opportunities afforded her champions and other leading performers, the U.S.A. has produced such men as Stan Stanczyk, the first to win three consecutive world titles at different bodyweights, and Tommy Kono, who won eight consecutive world and Olympic titles between 1952 and 1959.

In contrast, the current leading nation, the U.S.S.R., has many advantages over the U.S.A. In Russia, weight lifting is a major sport, with between 150,000 and 200,000 active participants (compared with perhaps 5,000 in the U.S.A.) and the State provides all the financial aid, training and other facilities that are necessary to keep them on top of the weight-lifting world.

The other iron-curtain countries follow the same pattern and it is the customary procedure to send the national team to a training camp for several weeks prior to a world championships – something that never happens in countries outside the Soviet bloc.

CHAPTER THIRTEEN

International rules of competition

EVERY weight lifter should have a thorough knowledge of the rules of competition. This may sound elementary, as ignorance of the various methods of procedure, rules appertaining to the lifts, etc., can easily lead to a situation in which one's chances of winning a title or contest are jeopardized. Yet I have known some active weight lifters who haven't taken the trouble to study fully the essential points governing performances.

Bodyweight Classes

In modern competition there are seven bodyweight classes, providing opportunities for men of all weights.

This gives the small men a chance of championship honours and recognition – as in sports like wrestling and boxing – whereas in some major sports like athletics, for example, the small man has to compete against his larger brothers, without any allowance for size or bodyweight, and is thus at a distinct disadvantage.

Here are details of the international classes:

Bantamweight. Up to a limit of 56 kilos (123¼ lb.).

Featherweight. From 56 kilos to 60 kilos (132¼ lb.).

Lightweight. From 60 kilos to 67½ kilos (148¾ lb.).

Middleweight. From 67½ kilos to 75 kilos (165¼ lb.).

Lightheavyweight. From 75 kilos to 82½ kilos (181¾ lb.).

Midheavyweight. From 82½ kilos to 90 kilos (198¼ lb.).

Heavyweight. All over 90 kilos.

Competitors must weigh (completely stripped) within the class limit in which they wish to compete, and are not allowed to take part in any class other than that of their ascertained bodyweight.

The weigh-in must take place within one hour of the scheduled time of the start of the competition, and must be supervised by the referee in charge of that particular class.

In the U.S., there are opportunities of competition in other bodyweight classes, too, and even competition between men of widely-differing weights.

Competitions between lifters of varying bodyweights are also staged (mainly in league lifting and friendly contests) on a bodyweight formula, or handicap system, but in world and Olympic championships and all types of international lifting, only the seven recognized Olympic bodyweight classes are used.

The other methods I have discussed apply normally to domestic lifting in this and other countries, and give a wider range of opportunity to the competitive weight lifter.

The Bar-bell

With weight lifting practised in so many countries, obviously it is necessary to use standardized equipment so that lifts performed in any part of the world have the same relative value.

Not only the bar-bell, of course, but other conditions of competition must be on the same level to the best of human endeavour.

International rules demand that a bar-bell with disc weights is the only authorized apparatus.

The modern appliance is normally a precision job, with the bar itself made of top-quality steel and the discs machined to accurate weight.

Standard dimensions are set as follows:

Length of bar, 210 centimetres (82.67 in.); distance between inside collars, 120 centimetres (47.24 in.); minimum diameter where knurled grips are placed, 2.8 centimetres (1.1 in.).

Maximum-sized discs (usually 20 kilos, or 45 or 50 lb.) measure 45 centimetres (17.72 in.).

This Olympic appliance, made to the same standard the world over, is invariably used in all major events. But in many minor championships (divisional, state, local, etc.) a more modest bar-bell set is used, mainly because of the comparatively high cost of the best appliance.

BEGINNERS' SCHEDULE FOR BODYBUILDERS

(*above*) Two Hands Curl. 2 (*above right*) Press from behind Neck. 3 (*right*) Deep Knees Bend (or Squat)

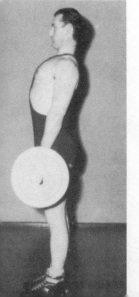

4 (*left and right*) Stiff-legged Dead Lift

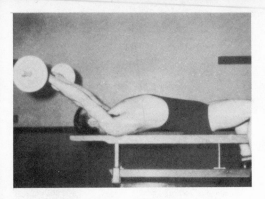

5 Straight-arm Pull Over on Bench

6 Press on Bench—starting position

8 Rise on Toes, on discs or blocks

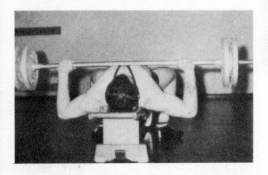

9 Bent-over Rowing Motion

7 Press on Bench—finishing position

10 (*above*) Alternate Press. 11 (*above right*) Front Squat

12 (*above*) Bent-arm Pull Over. 13 (*right*) Seated Press with Dumb-bells

14 (*left*) Bend Over Movement. 15 (*below*) Lateral Raise on Bench

REG PARK
(*Leeds, England*)

Winner of Mr. Britain
and Mr. Universe titles.

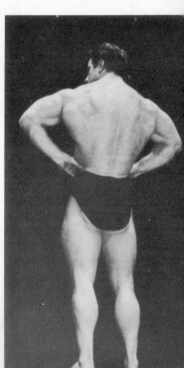

TWO HANDS CLEAN AND PRESS

16 Starting position for clean—arms locked, back straight, buttocks as low as comfort permits

17 Starting position for press—legs braced, hips forward a little, chest held high, slight layback

A good body position for ess, with acceptable layback

19 A position that could be passed or failed, according to the strictness of the officials

20 An obviously bad lift, with an exaggerated layback of upper body

21 A good starting position for split-style Snatch

24 The back foot touched down, the wrists beginning to turn

22 (*above*) Just starting the split movement, with bell at chest height—but rear foot has moved a little too soon. 23 (*below*) Both feet in mid-air, just prior to commencement of turning the wrists

25 An ideal split position—bar-bell directly over line of shoulders and hips, front knee well forward over toes

26 Squat-style Snatch. Note angle of trunk, with arms taken well back behind head to preserve position of bar-bell above centre of

TWO HANDS
CLEAN AND JERK

28 A good split clean, trunk upright, chest up and head back a little, front knee well forward

27 The full power of the arms and shoulders coming into action during the clean

29 Squat-style clean, full-depth position with elbows thrust forward to fix the bar-bell across the deltoids and to avoid touching knees

30 (*above*) The initial dip prior to the jerk, with elbows maintained in the same position.
31 (*right*) A strong, solid jerk, with bar-bell nicely balanced over line of shoulders and hips

SOME OF THE OTHER LIFTS AND ASSISTANCE EXERCISES

Demonstrated by the author

32 Two Hands Dead Lift—starting position

33 (*right*) Two Hands Dead Lift — finishing position

34 (*left*) One Hand Snatch, using a full-squat style and hook grip

35 (*right*) One Hand Swing, using a split style. The author's best official lifts in the Snatch and Swing are 140lb. on each, at just over 11-stone body-weight

36 Two very effective assistance exercises for Olympic lifting—high pulls for the Snatch and Clean, gaining maximum height by rising on toes

Many clubs and organizations use an ordinary 1-in. diameter bar with a revolving sleeve, and discs to correspond. This is permissible, providing that the standard measurements are met.

Platform

International rules demand that all lifts should be performed on a solid wooden platform measuring 4 by 4 metres (13.12 ft.) and that a lift will be valid only if performed within these limits.

Thus, if a lifter steps off the platform (even with only one foot) during the performance of a lift, he will be disqualified.

Adjudication

International and national events – that is the actual lifting part – are invariably controlled by three officials, a referee and two judges.

There are, naturally, other officials concerned in the running of the meeting, but only a referee and judges for controlling the lifting.

In world and Olympic championships, there is also a Jury of Appeal, which to some degree has control of the competition, having the power to reverse a desision (but not a unanimous one) on protest from the lifter concerned (via his manager or coach).

The referee is the chief official, and gives all necessary signals to the lifter for the commencement and conclusion of the lift. When the competitor has completed his lift and replaced the bar-bell on the platform, the referee and judges give their decisions by means of the lighting system provided.

This system consists of three white lights and three red lights, with each of the three officials having his own switches. If the official considers the lift to be good he will signal a white light. If considered not good he will signal a red light. For a lift to be good it must receive two or three white lights. Otherwise, the lift will be declared 'not good'. In other words, the majority decision will be the deciding factor.

If, as at some minor meetings, no lights are available, the method used is for the referee first to receive the verdicts of each judge and then give his own decision if necessary. Thus, if both judges agree on the validity or otherwise of a lift, then the referee announces their decision (which is already a majority, no matter what the referee's opinion is). If the judges disagree, then the referee's decision becomes the casting vote.

This system is by no means ideal and not to be compared with the lighting system, but has to suffice all the time a lighting system is not available at *all* meetings.

There are occasions when the adjudicating is done solely by a referee – meetings such as divisional and county championships, etc., when it is often difficult to obtain three officials.

This is permissible under some rules, and while opinion may be divided on the desirability of allowing one official to decide if a lift is good or not good it is mosty a matter of expediency, and does at least allow meetings to be held ; whereas if three officials were insisted on it might not be possible to stage some meetings. And, after all, some other sports are controlled by one official.

In Britain, referees are appointed by examination, a method that is not universally adopted by any means, many countries appointing referees only by virtue of their known experience.

Personally, as a former chairman of the British Referees' Examining Board, I consider our system of referee appointments to be about the best in the world, and while merely to pass an examination is no guarantee of producing a good official, at least it ensures that a man has some technical knowledge of the sport and is of reasonable intelligence.

On appointment, a British referee is graded as a divisional referee for a period of at least two years before being eligible for promotion to a national referee. Later, he can be appointed an international referee, with power to function at international meetings.

CHAPTER FOURTEEN

Competition procedure

EACH competitor in an Olympic championship has the privilege of three attempts for each of the scheduled lifts (but not necessarily for each weight attempted). The weight of the bar-bell must be in multiples of $2\frac{1}{2}$ kilos (or 5 lb. in countries using the English weight system). For world championships, irrespective of what country the championships are held in, the kilo system is used.

Weight Increases

The increase of weight between each attempt must not be less than 5 kilos (or 10 lb.), except for the last attempt, when it may be $2\frac{1}{2}$ kilos (or 5 lb.). If a competitor chooses to take just a $2\frac{1}{2}$-kilos increase between his first and second attempt, then this will be counted as his last attempt.

A larger increase than the minimum of 5 kilos (or $2\frac{1}{2}$ kilos on last attempt) can be taken. And, in fact, does happen quite frequently.

In no case will a competitor be allowed to take a weight less than that used in his preceding attempt. If three failures are made on any weight, then the competitor scores nothing for that particuar lift and is eliminated from the competition.

At the start of the competition, the bar-bell will be loaded to the lowest poundage required by any of the competitors, and must be kept rising in poundage as the competition proceeds, each lifter coming in at the poundage he wants on any particular attempt.

In no case can a poundage once attempted by any competitor be lowered for any other competitor.

When two competitors wish to take the same starting poundage for a scheduled lift, their names must be drawn by lot.

The competitor whose name is drawn first must lift first and continue to lift first (when both want the same poundage, of course) right to the end of the attempts.

If, during the following lift, both competitors wish to take the same starting poundage, the one who was first for the preceding lift must now be second. If the same situation arises for the third lift, then fresh lots must be drawn.

In the case of a tie in total between two or more competitors the lighter man (as taken at the weigh-in) will take the highest placing.

If the competitors were the same bodyweight at the weigh-in, then they must be weighed again after the competition, the bodyweights thus obtained being the deciding factor. If there is again equality in bodyweight then the competitors will be declared as equal rating.

Rising weight

Dealing now with these rules in more detail, we see that the fundamental principle is that the weight is kept constantly rising as the competitors take their attempts, with the weaker ones coming in first and perhaps even completing their three attempts before many of the stronger competitors commence.

While in certain circumstances this procedure does tend to slow down the proceedings (as for example, when only one competitor wants a particular weight and he lifts alone with permitted rests between attempts), from the spectators' point of view it provides a spectacle of ascending interest as the weaker performers fall out and the stronger ones battle it out as the weight approaches maximum.

It will be seen that the competitor who lifts last on any of the lifts has the advantage of knowing exactly what he has to do in order to equal or beat his rivals as circumstances warrant.

Particularly is this important on the Clean and Jerk, when the final phases of the contest are being decided, and often we see one competitor who has started higher on this lift and has a chance of winning the title, waiting until everyone has finished to ascertain what he needs in order to win and asking for that poundage.

Record Breaking

In the same way as Olympic champions are recognized at world, continental, national, area and district levels, so are records on each of the Olympic lifts and totals.

Normally a record on an individual lift can be attempted at any time and on any occasion, unlike the winning of an

Olympic title, which must be won at a properly organized contest for that particular title.

Conditions governing record totals vary, inasmuch as a world-record total must be set up at a world championships, Olympic Games, any other international meeting, or a national championships.

Dealing first with world records, we find that they are graded in the same bodyweight classes as for championships.

Records on individual lifts are recorded in multiples of $\frac{1}{2}$ kilo, which is also the minimum stage of increase from one record to another.

A record weight is weighed to the nearest $\frac{1}{2}$ kilo downwards – thus a bar-bell weighing 92 kilos 600 grammes will be recorded as $92\frac{1}{2}$ kilos, and for any further record the minimum weight required will be 93 kilos.

Majority Verdict

For recognition of a world record, the lift must be passed by a majority of the three presiding officials, i.e. referee and two judges, who must be of International standard.

Not so long ago a unanimous verdict was essential before any record could be recognized, but this rule was changed to come into line with the procedure for championships lifting where a lifter can accumulate a total (perhaps even a *record* total) and yet have only a majority verdict on each of his lifts.

Most world records are, of course, put up at such major events as world championships, international contests, etc., but as I stated earlier can be made on any suitable occasion. The question of weighing-in is important in this respect and differs from the procedure for championships, when competitors are weighed beforehand.

For record breaking, the lifter must be weighed immediately *after* breaking a record in order to ascertain his exact weight at the time of performance.

It will readily be seen that in a championship meeting, when a lifter can weigh-in an hour or more before actually lifting, he could weigh over his class-weight limit when actually performing.

This, in fact, does very often happen, particularly in the case of a lifter who has had trouble in making weight and then immediately after the weigh-in, has a good meal. Lifters have been known to put on two or three pounds from the weigh-in to the time when they take their first attempt in the championship.

In the case of a record, however, it is very important that a man should actually weigh within the limits of his class when he makes his record lift.

The bar-bell should also be weighed to ascertain the exact poundage, and not taken at its face value. A modern international appliance seldom weighs *exactly* its face value at every poundage stage.

When competing in a world or Olympic championship, a lifter will normally be allowed only one attempt at a world record and then only if he comes near this poundage during the course of the competition. If, of course, he commences lifting at or near a world-record figure, he would be allowed more than one attempt as he is entitled to at least three attempts for his actual championship effort.

When competing for world records on other occasions, there is actually no rule of the International Federation governing the number of permitted attempts, and generally it is left to the time available and the discretion of the organizers and officials of the particular event.

Record Claims

The Secretary-General of the International Federation keeps a register of world records, and claims signed by the presiding officials (also the President or Secretary of the national body concerned) must be sent to him within a maximum period of two months.

There are some differences in this country concerning British and lesser records as compared with world records.

First, the bodyweight classes. World records are recognized in the seven international bodyweight classes, from bantamweight through to heavyweight. These classes are, of course, also recognized in Britain, but as I said earlier, in addition we recognize records in a completely different range of bodyweight classes, viz., even-stone from 8 stone through to 14 stone.

Many of you may wonder why this is so. Actually, the even-stone classes are traditionally the basic British classes, dating back to the early days of the British Amateur Weight Lifters' Association when British Amateur Championships were the main interest of our national lifting.

Olympic Trials

In those early days, Olympic Championships were rarely held and were termed Olympic Trials, staged shortly before an Olympic Games was due. The real interest in Olympic lifting didn't come until the early 1930's, in the days of such lifters as Ron Walker and Norman Holroyd, who were considered as world prospects and fostered a greater interest in Olympic lifting.

British Amateur Championships were decided on all-round lifting, usually four or five lifts that were changed every year, but eventually Olympic lifting became the major interest and about a decade ago the character of the Amateur Championships was changed when they, too, were decided on the Olympic lifts. This gave us two championships a year, with the Olympics held in the spring or summer and the Amateurs in the autumn or winter. Later, the Amateur Championships were abolished altogether, to be replaced by the Strength Set, a form of lifting that is still gaining in popularity.

Naturally, when championships were being held in the even-stone classes, records were also recognized. Remember, too, that we recognize all our thirty-one lifts in even-stone classes, with only the international lifts in international bodyweight classes as well. In this way, a record on an Olympic lift often is twofold, as, for example, when a middleweight record is made, it is often also a 12-stone record.

Record Differences

A difference in British record breaking concerns the poundage multiples.

I have explained that the International Federation practice for world records is to register them in muliples of half a kilo

(1.1 English pounds) and with a minimum increase of the same multiple before a new record can be set up. But in Britain we register poundages in multiples of a quarter-pound and stipulate that for a British record only on the Olympic lifts the minimum increase on an old record must be one pound.

However, for lesser records on the Olympic lifts, such as divisional and county (and for all records on the remaining lifts) a quarter-pound is the minimum margin.

British and lesser records may be attempted at any time – in clubs, at championships, league and friendly contests, etc. – the only stipulation being that the lifter is a registered member of the governing body, the scales used are in good working order and have been certified as such during the current year, and that qualified officials adjudicate on the record attempts.

For British records, three officials are required, with the referee of national grade. The judges need not be national, divisional standard being considered sufficient.

For divisional and other records one referee is sufficient, either national or divisional grade.

Similar to the procedure for world record breaking a majority verdict is sufficient for recognition of a new record. The bar-bell and the lifter must be weighed immediately after the creation of any new record.

Three Attempts in Public

Any number of attempts may be made on a record poundage, except when lifting in a public display, when the number of attempts is limited to three. This rule, obviously, is to prevent the possibility of countless abortive attempts being made before the public.

In addition to individual lifts, records are also recognized on Olympic totals in both international and even-stone classes, and similarly may be made at any time. Only the usual three attempts on each lift, with the proper increases observed, may be made.

Kilo Conversion

If a world record is made in this country, using our traditional pound scales, the weight must be converted into kilos, to the nearest half-kilo downwards, so that a proper submission may be made to the International Federation.

Thus, as an example, a bar-bell which weighs 288 lb. is actually 130.63 kilos when converted, but must be recorded as 130½ kilos. In such a case the lifter actually loses credit for .13 of a kilo, but must necessarily do so in order to comply with international regulations. The British record will naturally be recorded to the full 288 lb.

CHAPTER FIFTEEN

Rules of the Olympic lifts

HERE are the rules governing performance of the three Olympic lifts, taken from the official handbook of the International Weight-lifting Federation, together with necessary clarification and comment.

TWO HANDS CLEAN AND PRESS

The Clean

The bar-bell shall be placed horizontally in front of the lifter's legs, gripped palms downwards, and brought to the shoulders in a distinct movement while either splitting or bending the legs.

The bar-bell shall rest on the clavicles, the chest, or on the arms fully bent, with the feet together or apart on the same line, with the legs straight.

A lifter who is not able to rest the bar-bell on his chest must inform the three judges before the beginning of the contest. In this case, the bar-bell shall be brought to the level of the sterno-clavicular bone.

The referee should wait until the lifter is motionless and in a position of stability, then immediately give the signal (with a clap of the hands) to start the press proper. If the lifter moves his feet after the signal has been given, even if the arms are not extended, the lift must be disqualified.

The Press

The referee having given the signal, the bar-bell shall be lifted until the arms are completely extended, without any jerk or pause, bending of the legs, excessive backward bending of the body or displacement or movement of the feet.

The final position shall be held, the lifter remaining motionless until the referee gives the signal to return the bar-bell to the ground.

It is appreciated that some differences of opinion will always be present when the slight leaning back permitted is considered. However, providing the lean-back is directed to driving the bar-bell vertically upwards, then the lift is good. Excessive, or continued bending of the back is cause for disqualification.

Incorrect Movements

1. Cleaning in several movements. In this case the referee should not give the starting signal and should order the bar-bell to be returned to the ground.

2. Starting the press before the referee has given the signal.

3. Any bending, however little, of the legs before or during the press.

4. Flexing of the arms after the referee's signal.

5. Flexing the body by bending or extension.

6. Leaning backwards excessively under the bar-bell.

7. Uneven extension of the arms.

8. Pause during extension of the arms.

9. Incomplete extension of the arms.

10. Twisting of the body.

11. Moving the feet.

12. Rising on toes or heels.

13. Returning the bar-bell to the ground before the referee's signal.

Although these rules generally are quite clear, there are several points that need some discussion to provide further clarification – also in relation to the different interpretations that are made by lifters and officials from the many countries in which weight lifting is practised . . . and indeed from among lifters and officials from the same country.

I will go through all the points as they arise in order of performing the lift, taking the 'clean' part first. There are rarely any complications in this stage, although we do sometimes see lifters disqualified during this early phase of the lift.

The taking of the bar-bell from the platform to the commencing position for the press should be made in one distinct and clean movement, with the bar-bell coming to rest at the point from which the press is to be made.

This point can be anywhere between the line of the nipples and the top of the sternum bone. Take note that the bar-bell must rest on the body and not be held away from it, unless a lifter is so physically constructed that he is unable to rest the bar-bell on his chest.

In such a case, the lifter is allowed to hold the bar-bell away from his chest on a line level with the top of the sternum.

It is not permitted to clean the bar-bell to a point, say, just above the nipples in the first movement and then move it further up the chest to adopt the commencing position for the press, as this obviously constitutes two movements.

Another point to remember is that a lifter can also be disqualified if the bar-bell touches any part of the thighs or body before coming in to the chest. Such instances are rare and even so, my experience is that many referees do not disqualify a lifter for this fault.

It is true that touching of the bar-bell on the thighs or body is no help to the lifter (in fact, it is more of a hindrance). But the rules are clear enough. The movement must be 'clean' above the knees.

As soon as the pressing position is adopted, and the lifter is motionless, the referee will give the signal for the press to commence.

This starting position must be held without any exaggerated body-lean and with the legs braced and held on a level plane (that is, with both feet on a line parallel with the lifter's front).

Immediately the referee's signal is given, the lifter is free to press the bar-bell in his own time. For practically every lifter that will be as soon as possible after the signal in order not to hold the weight for an unnecessarily long period.

There are a few lifters who seem to be able to press better by delaying their start for a few seconds, but these are exceptional cases.

If the lifter, after receiving the referee's signal, then adopts a different body position by leaning either backwards or forwards before starting to press the bar-bell, he invites disqualification.

After the press has been started the lifter is allowed to lean backwards to a degree that is not exaggerated. If he already held a backwards bend in his starting position that was as much as could be permitted, then obviously he must not lean back any farther.

Some lifters, however, adopt a fairly upright position at the commencement of the press, so they will be permitted to lean back during the press to a further extent.

A Controversial Rule

This clause of the rule which defines the permitted lean-back as 'not exaggerated' is in my view a weak spot, because it is virtually impossible to get any universal agreement or interpretation as to what constitutes 'exaggerated'.

The rules do say that provided the lean-back is directed to driving the bar-bell vertically upwards, then the lift is good. But with so many different physical types, there are certainly many differences in the body positions adopted, with some lifters able to adopt a considerable backbend while still driving the bar-bell vertically upwards.

Some lifters try to 'get away' with a pressing movement that is aided with a quick leaning forwards of the body, immediately followed by a leaning back as the press is made. This is not allowed.

Others try to gain an impetus to the start of the press by dropping the bar-bell an inch or two (sometimes combined with an unlocking of the knees and/or a dropping of the shoulders) then immediately driving the bar-bell upwards. None of these manoeuvres is permitted, either.

The press must be started purely by the pressing muscles of the arms and shoulders (combined legally, of course, with contractions of the essential bracing muscle groups of the thighs, buttocks and lower back). This is not only the letter of the law, but the spirit as well.

Such manoeuvres as I have mentioned are made only in an attempt to gain extra pounds and in the hope that the officials will be lenient enough to allow them.

The other points regarding the bar-bell stopping during the pressing movement, uneven extension of the arms, feet movement, rising on the toes or heels, twisting the body or failure to hold the bar-bell in the concluding position for the referee's signal, are clear enough and need no further comment.

TWO HANDS SNATCH

The Two Hands Snatch, second of the three Olympic movements, does not have the adjudication problems of the Press, and consequently there is much less variation in the standard of officiating. There are a few points, however, that require some discussion and clarification. But first, the international rules:

The bar-bell shall be placed horizontally in front of the lifter's legs. It shall be gripped, palms downwards, and pulled in one movement from the ground to the full extent of the arms vertically above the head, while either splitting or bending the legs.

The bar-bell shall pass with a continuous movement along the body, of which no part other than the feet shall touch the ground during the execution of the movement.

The weight which has been lifted must be held in the final position of immobility, the arms and legs extended, the feet on the same line, until the referee gives the signal to return the bar-bell to the ground.

Important remark: The turning over of the wrists must not occur before the bar-bell has passed the top of the lifter's head.

The lifter may recover his legs in his own time.

Incorrect Movements
1. Cleaning from the hang.
2. Pause during the lifting of the bar-bell.
3. Movements of hands along the bar-bell during execution of the lift.
4. Uneven extension of the arms.
5. Incomplete extension of the arms.
6. Movement finishing with a press-out.
7. Flexing and extension of the arms while regaining legs.
8. Touching the ground with the knee.
9. Leaving the platform.
10. Grounding the bar-bell before the referee's signal.

It will be seen that the fundamental principle of the Snatch is that it shall be a clean and continuous movement, so that once the bar-bell has left the platform it must travel non-stop to arms' length.

The clause of the rules concerning the pressing-out of the bar-bell is the one that does give some variation of interpretation.

Generally, a press-out can occur under the following circumstances: (*a*) When the wrists are turned over too soon, i.e.

before the bar-bell has passed the top of the lifter's head, and (b) when the bar-bell is pulled not quite to full locked arms, stops momentarily, and the movement then completed by pressing out.

The fundamental reason for both these causes of disqualification is the failure to pull the bar-bell high enough in the first stage of the lift before the split or squat movement is started, often combined with a slowness of movement in reaching the necessary full split or squat position to fix the weight on locked arms.

In case (a), the turning over of the wrists has to be closely watched by the referee and judges to ensure that the movement is technically correct, because as the wrists turn, the head and body of the lifter will be moving downwards as the bar-bell is travelling upwards.

This means that until the referee has had some experience of watching for this particular point it isn't particularly easy in some instances to spot the exact relative position of the bar-bell to the head.

However, it will be found, generally, that if the wrists turn over too soon, the bar-bell will be pressed out from the line of the top of the head (or even lower) and will appear as a lengthy and slowish press-out.

In case (b), often it will be found that a lifter will quite properly delay the turning over of his wrists until the bar-bell is clear of the top of the head, yet still be unable to prevent the bar-bell stopping before it reaches locked arms.

Apart from the obvious fact that the weight may just be too heavy, one major reason for this type of failure is that the lifter doesn't lower his body fast enough, or low enough (or both) into the split or squat position in order to affect a snappy arm lock, so if the bar-bell stops before reaching locked arms and is then raised higher by a press-out movement, then that clearly is not a good lift.

The other points for disqualification listed above are fairly clear and don't need further clarification – except perhaps points 5 and 7.

Point 5 refers to a lifter snatching the bar-bell *almost* to arms' length, then recovering to the erect position still holding the bar-bell on arms that are not quite locked.

Point 7 refers to instances when a lifter quite correctly takes the bar-bell to full locked arms but allows his arms to unlock a noticeable amount, then proceeds immediately to lock them again, or even a few seconds later while recovering to the erect position.

This, of course, constitutes two attempts at locking the arms and is cause for disqualification.

Two Hands Clean and Jerk

The final lift of the Olympic three and generally without many controversial points. I have made comments on the points that do sometimes cause variations of adjudication.

First, the international rules:

First Part – Clean

The bar shall be placed horizontally in front of the lifter's legs. It shall be gripped, palms downwards, and pulled up in a single movement from the ground to the shoulders, while either splitting or bending the legs.

The bar must not touch the chest before the final position ; it shall then rest on the clavicles, on the chest or on the arms fully bent.

The feet shall be returned to the same line, legs straight, before the jerk is begun. The lifter may do this in his own time.

Second Part – Jerk

Bend the legs and then extend them, as well as the arms, so as to bring the bar to the full stretch of the arms vertically extended.

Return the feet to the same line, arms and legs extended and await the referee's signal to return the bar to the ground.

After the clean and before the jerk, the lifter is allowed to make sure of the position of the bar.

Incorrect Movements (i) Clean

1. Any apparent effort of pulling.
2. Cleaning from the hang.
3. Touching the ground with the knee.

4. Any clean in which the bar touches the body before its final position at the shoulders.

5. Cleaning while bending; touching the knees with the elbows.

6. Leaving the platform.

(ii) Jerk

1. Any apparent jerking.
2. Uneven extension of the arms.
3. Pause during extension of the arms.
4. Flexing and extension of the arms.
5. Leaving the platform.
6. Grounding the bar before the referee's signal.

The first point to consider on the clean is (1) of 'incorrect movements' – that is, any apparent effort of cleaning.

Sometimes a lifter will start the movement by actually raising the bar a distance from the platform, then change his mind ; maybe because of indecision or perhaps because the bar feels one-sided due to incorrect hand spacing, or maybe because it just feels too heavy.

Many lifters and officials believe that an attempt is not made until the bar has reached knees' height. There is a F.I.H.C. ruling (under general rules for all lifts) that 'The referee will declare as not passed any attempt not finished, when strain has visibly been exerted, and in particular those attempts in which the bar has arrived at the height of the knee.'

It is clear from this that if the bar has been lifted even only a few inches and the referee considers strain has been exerted in the attempt, then the lift is not good and must be considered as an attempt.

It is permitted, of course, to test the weight before attempting the lift by raising the bar from the platform a few inches – and many lifters do carry out this practice. Referees must not be confused by this and generally it is fairly obvious what the lifter is doing.

Another major point to consider on the clean is that concerning the arrival of the bar at the chest or shoulders. Notice that the rules state: 'The bar must not touch the chest before the final position and shall then rest on the clavicles, chest or the arms fully bent.'

The interpretation here is that wherever the bar-bell is first pulled to, then that is the position from which it shall be jerked.

Most lifters pull the bar-bell right up to the clavicles at the top of the chest, but we do sometimes see lifters clean the bar to a point lower than this.

This is permissible, but once the bar touches the chest then it must not be moved farther up prior to the clean. In all cases the minimum height must be that of the line of the nipples.

The lifter is allowed to make sure of a comfortable position for the bar-bell either at the chest or the shoulders by a slight movement or readjustment, but referees must watch this closely to ensure that it is only a settlement of the bar-bell and not an obvious moving up to any great extent.

On the jerk, one of the major points to watch is (1) any apparent jerking. I remember much controversy over the position of a lifter making his initial dip of the body prior to the actual jerk, then changing his mind, stopping and preparing himself for a further effort. This constitutes an attempt . . . and should be ruled out.

As it is not possible to jerk near-limit or limit poundages without making a preliminary body dip, then this movement must be considered as part of the attempt to jerk the bar-bell. So if the lifter makes this dip, then stops and starts again it must be construed as an attempt not finished and accordingly disqualified.

During the actual jerking movement after the bar-bell has left the shoulders, notice that Rule 3 does not permit any pause during the extension of the arms.

A press-out finish is permitted . . . that is, the bar-bell can slow down during the extension of the arms (but without actually stopping) and the movement completed by pressing out.

Rule 4 of the jerk concerns a lift in which the arms lock correctly, but then unlock and relock. This is not permitted.

One further point (and this applies to all lifts). If, after the referee's signal to return the bar-bell to the platform, the lifter allows the bar-bell to fall to the platform, the lift will be declared not passed.

How to perform the Two Hands Clean and Press

OLYMPIC weight lifting is probably governed by more rigid rules than any other sport, and while within the framework of these rules there is scope for individual style and technique on the three lifts, there is, inevitably, some restriction.

Weight-lifting coaches constantly endeavour to teach their pupils the best possible technique for the performance of the various lifts, but occasionally they become a little over zealous in encouraging them to perform their lifts in a style that is contrary in some respects to the rules.

Adjudication on Olympic lifting, generally, isn't so strict as the rule book demands, particularly on the Press. Many lifts that are passed transgress the strict letter of the law to some degree.

The standard of adjudication varies so much internationally – and even in one particular country – that a lifter will sometimes get lifts passed that are not technically correct. But obviously there is a risk of lifting in any style that one knows is 'suspect'.

When such a lifter competes under stricter adjudication he will almost certainly have his lifts disqualified.

A classic example of this was the experience of the Australian weight lifters at the 1960 Olympic Games, when several of them failed with all their attempts on the Press and were eliminated from the competition.

In their own country, the Australians had been accustomed to pressing in a style that was normally accepted by the judges. But with the stricter standards found at the Olympic Games on this occasion, this style was not acceptable.

As an international referee myself, but one who also lifts and does some coaching, I encourage lifting techniques that, while taking every advantage of the standard of adjudication and the varying interpetation of the rules, will also ensure that lifts will be passed by even the stricter types of judges.

In my view there is no one method of pressing that will suit everyone, bearing in mind the many different types of physiques found among weight lifters.

The varying arm lengths, proportion of upper arms to forearms, breadth of shoulders, length of back and degrees of shoulder suppleness make it obvious that every individual cannot be expected to lift in *exactly* the same style and movement.

And while I stressed earlier that the somewhat rigid rules of the sport do restrict individual styles, there is still scope for variations from what could be called an average or normal style of pressing.

I suggest that a beginner should first use the method I will describe and which I consider to be the most effective for the majority of lifters. Then, as progress is made, he should experiment with some variations, such as employing a different starting position, slightly wider or narrower hand grip or a different elbows' action.

The comparative strength of the main pressing groups of muscles – the deltoids and triceps, together with the bracing muscles of the back and legs – has some effect, too, on the position to be adopted.

For example, some lifters find they are able to start the press from the shoulders fairly easily but have great difficulty in completing the final stage of the movement, once they have got the bar-bell past the normally hardest middle part of the lift.

Such lifters often find a slightly-wider grip enables them to improve this weakness – as a fairly wide grip, although making it a little harder to start the bar-bell moving from the shoulders, makes that part of the lift from about eyes' level to arms' length a little easier.

On the other hand, a lifter who finds the second phase of the movement easier might do better to adopt a narrower grip.

A fair trial for a reasonable time with various grip positions will decide for you the best grip to adopt.

But for a start, use my recommended method. Of course, any specific muscular weakness cannot be overcome, either partially or fully, simply by adopting a different mechanical position.

Special attention must be given to any deficiency by practising supplementary exercises and variations of the pressing movement. (See later chapter on this type of work.)

Here is the complete method of performance.

A study of the rules (see previous chapter) will have shown you that the lift is divided into two movements. First, the clean to the shoulders, then the actual press to arms' length.

The first part of the lift shouldn't normally present any difficulty or complication, as the weight that one can press from the shoulders is usually so much lighter than the weight that can be cleaned.

However, there is a very small minority of lifters who can press almost as much as they can clean and this type of lifter should give special attention to improving his cleaning power so that he doesn't have to waste so much physical or mental energy in this first stage of the lift.

Psychologically it is important that the weight should feel light as it is pulled into the shoulders, as automatically one then feels confident that the press will be successful. If, on the other hand, the weight feels heavy, a doubt is likely to be felt immediately, and the power of the mind is a far more important factor than many people realize.

To perform the Press, first place the feet close up to the bar-bell – with the shins just a couple of inches or so away – and spaced with the heels 12–16 in. apart, according to one's height. The feet can be placed closer or wider apart, or even together if desired, but I recommend the spacing as specified as giving the most solid base from which to press.

Straight away grasp the bar-bell, using either a normal or a thumbless grip.

The normal grip is with the thumb circling the bar-bell in the opposite direction to the fingers, and is perhaps the most popular. But there are many lifters who use the thumbless grip, in which the thumb follows the line of the fingers.

On this lift, I don't think there is any special point that makes ither of these grips any more effective than the other, and feel hat primarily it is a matter of comfort. And this can be decided only by giving each of the methods a fair trial.

Adopt the starting position as shown in Plate 16 with

buttocks fairly low, back and arms straight and head held up in line with the spine.

Concentrate for just a second or two before starting the lift, as holding this position for too long a period can cause some slight muscle fatigue in the legs ; also, when the waiting period is unduly extended, one's concentration is apt to become indecisive and makes the wait even longer by not being able to make up one's mind just when to start the lift.

Except for a very small minority of lifters it will not be necessary to move the feet in order to clean the weight, so you must make sure that you have placed your feet in exactly the position from which you intend to press.

The clean movement is made by a strong leg drive combined with the pulling power of the arms and shoulders. It must be made vigorously in order to assist in making the movement feel light, as stressed earlier.

Start the movement by a vigorous straightening of the legs, leading upwards simultaneously with the head and buttocks, pulling the bar-bell close to the body and turning it into the shoulders with a backward flip of the wrists and a thrusting forwards of the elbows.

The main pulling power of the arms should not start until the bar-bell is felt to be clear of the floor, making the stronger legs and back perform the hardest part of overcoming the inertia of the bar-bell and raising it clear of the floor.

In the clean for the Clean and Jerk lift, this movement has greater importance owing to the heavier weight being handled, but even when lifting the lighter weights used in the Press, it is important to make the movement as easy as possible in order to conserve your energy and strength for the essential pressing part of the lift.

As the bar-bell is being turned into the shoulders, make the movement a little easier by using a slight dip of the body by bending the knees to receive the bar-bell at the shoulders. This movement should be about a quarter-squat ; there is no need to dip the body any lower, except in the case of lifters who have unusual difficulty in cleaning their pressing weights.

Co-ordinated breathing is important and I have found the best method is to inhale as the clean is made, exhaling as the bar-bell settles at the shoulders.

Then, if the pressing stance is adopted with the minimum of delay, you will be ready to inhale again when the referee gives the signal to commence the press.

Although the rules permit the bar-bell to be pressed from any part of the upper chest – but only from the point where the bar-bell touches the chest when it is cleaned – I recommend the highest position, right in the base of the throat, with the bar-bell resting on top of the sternum bone.

Some lifters hold the bar-bell at varying points between the line at the top of the nipples and the position I advocate, in order to obtain a longer drive. A lower position can be tried, of course, but I am sure the one I recommend will be found to be the best for most lifters.

As soon as the bar-bell is brought to the starting position for the press, straighten the legs from the dip you have used to facilitate the cleaning movement and set yourself for the referee's signal.

If you adopt a fair amount of lean-back at the start of the movement, then you will not be permitted to accentuate this during the actual press. But if you use just a little lean-back, sufficient to allow the bar-bell to be pressed in a vertical line past the face, then you still have a margin left to lean back a little farther as the bar-bell hits the sticking point of the press – midway through the movement when the bar-bell is approximately at forehead level.

I believe that this slight lean-back as the bar-bell slows down is more useful than to keep the bar-bell moving than in the initial stage of the lift, using the maximum amount of lay back that is permitted. So I recommend a little lay-back at the start of the press, then a little more when the bar-bell reaches the midway position of the press.

The forearms should be held almost vertical and the hips taken slightly forwards so that the body forms a slight curve from the head to the heels, with the shoulders almost directly above the heels, or maybe just a little farther backwards (see Plate 17).

With the bar-bell grasped well down in the heel of the hand – for greater power – the weight will be held over a line through the bones of the forearms – the strongest position for pressing.

The body should be held braced although not quite at full tension. Then, as soon as the referee's signal is heard, commence to press and at the same time fully tense the thighs and buttocks.

This full tension of the thighs and buttocks is of utmost importance because it provides a solid base for pressing.

Any slackness of posture while pressing a limit or near-limit weight will lead to a sagging of the trunk and an exaggerated lean-back. This can easily be checked by trial. Press a heavy weight as I recommend. Rest a few moments. Then try the lift again – without contracting the thighs and buttocks – and note the difference.

Regarding breathing at this stage of the lift, I recommend that you breathe in as you start the pressing movement although many lifters prefer to inhale before the press is commenced. Again, this is a matter for personal preference and a fair trial should be given to both methods.

But whatever method is finally adopted, I must warn against the danger of holding the breath for any prolonged period. Holding the breath too long can sometimes cause a tendency to dizziness and 'blacking out'. So watch this carefully.

The modern method of pressing is to start the bar-bell moving as fast as possible, the lifter 'exploding' into action immediately he hears the referee's signal.

A fast Press is permissible, but care must be taken to ensure that the start of the lift is fair and not accompanied by any unlocking of the knees, dropping of the bar-bell before it starts on its upwards movement, or any swaying of the body.

Press the bar-bell directly upwards. With the head held backwards a little as described earlier, there is no possibility of the bar-bell touching the face or of it having to be pressed round the face in a slightly curved movement.

Keep the bar-bell moving as fast as possible and ease the elbows outwards as it nears the top of the head. This position is the hardest part of the lift, and as the bar-bell strikes this 'sticking point', the tendency will be for it to stop when using a heavy weight.

A further lean back of the body, combined with a slight easing forward of the hips will help to keep the bar-bell moving (and to preserve the centre of gravity of the bar-bell over the body as in the starting position) . . . unless, of course, the weight is beyond your limit.

But remember the rules ; any lean-back must not be 'exaggerated'. A study of Plates 18, 19 and 20 will show the difference between an acceptable lift and one that contravenes the rules.

When leaning back endeavour to make the movement as much as possible from the upper part of the body, keeping the chest high and allowing the shoulders to drop slightly as the bar-bell passes the line of the top of the head.

Effort and determination is the keynote here. Fight to keep the bar-bell moving and to avoid any excessive lean-back. Concentrate on keeping the knees tightly locked and the thighs braced to the maximum extent.

As the bar-bell nears the locked arms' position, bring the body nearer the upright position again, approximating the stance adopted at the start of the lift.

This style is very similar to that used by many of the world's record holders and other top-line performers.

One of the most favoured variations from this method of pressing is to adopt a maximum layback at the start of the press, with the elbows taken back as far as possible and the chest held very high. Then, as the press is being made, to bring the trunk up to an upright position to coincide with the locking of the arms.

Many of the world's leading pressers use this method, with slight variations according to their physical capabilities.

Not everyone can use it, nor does everyone favour it. Nevertheless, it is worth an extended trial. In fact, any variation from the method I have recommended for a beginner deserves a trial, because as I have stressed, everyone cannot be expected to perform in exactly the same way. Only the individual, with the co-operation of his coach, can decide finally which method will suit him best.

If you have used the method of inhaling as the press is started you will have filled your lungs as the lift is completed. Then, as you are holding your position for the referee's signal, exhale.

If you have taken a breath before pressing it is advisable to start exhaling as the bar-bell breaks through the 'sticking point' and nears locked arms.

Remember that you must hold the bar-bell motionless in the concluding position for a slight pause. But don't on any account anticipate this pause yourself. Wait to hear the referee's signal before lowering the bar-bell to the platform.

CHAPTER SEVENTEEN

How to perform the Two Hands Snatch

THE Snatch is considered by many authorities to be the most attractive of all weight-lifting movements – the acme of skill, strength and speed. In fact, the lift is the complete answer to critics who say that weight lifting is a sport only for the slow and cumbersome.

Strength is the essential requirement – as in all weight lifting. Nevertheless, speed and good technique is of particular importance, when so much depends on precision of movement, timing, balance and co-ordination. All these qualities will enable a lifter to make maximum use of his available strength.

The rules demand that the bar-bell shall be lifted from the platform to arms' length overhead in one clean and continuous movement but in contrast to what I have said about the Press, there is, generally, little variation in the standard of adjudication for the Snatch and less diversity of interpretation of the rules of performance.

The main cause of disqualification – apart from the obvious one of knee-touching – is completing the lift with a press-out movement, normally easy enough for an experienced judge to see.

Two distinct styles are favoured: the split-style, in which one leg is moved forwards, one backwards, to facilitate the lowering of the body under the bar-bell ; and the squat-style, in which the lifter drops into a squat, or deep-knees-bend position, in order to fix the bar-bell overhead.

Most lifters use the split method although the number of devotees of the squat style is increasing.

I believe that the split style is more suitable for most lifters, but that the alternative style has greater poundage possibilities for the performer who is physically suited to this method of lifting.

Generally I have found that the percentage of failures is greater among squat snatchers, and believe that this is largely because many performers use this method when in fact they would be more suited to the split style.

Essential requirements for a squat snatcher are mobile shoulder joints and a delicate sense of balance, together with fast reflex actions.

Without these qualities a lifter would be better advised to use the split method, which in my view is safer and offers greater latitude for recovery in the event of a lift not being fixed overhead in a correctly-balanced position.

Here is my recommended method of performance for the split-style Snatch.

The feet spacing should be narrower than in the Press – 6–9 in. between the heels. Stand close up to the bar-bell and take your handgrip with the hands spaced fairly wide apart.

For most lifters I consider a wide grip to be essential, with the outsides of the hands only about two or three inches from the collars of the bar-bell.

Although, theoretically, a wide handgrip is said to lessen the power of the pull, experience has proved that most lifters obtain better results with a wide or even a maximum-width grip.

The normal handgrip is taken with thumbs round the barbell as previously described in the Press, but many lifters prefer the 'hook' grip, in which the first one or two fingers are gripped over the thumb to lock it. Only lifters with fairly long fingers can successfully use this method.

In the starting position the back should be flat, buttocks held as low as comfort permits, arms straight, shoulders a little forward of the hands.

This is the best mechanical position to obtain maximum results. But the position will vary according to one's physical make-up and disposition of strength. For example, a lifter with long thighs and a short body will find he can obtain a stronger leg drive by holding a slightly higher position of the buttocks, while a lifter who is relatively stronger in the back than the legs will get a stronger drive by also adopting this position.

Although the Snatch is made in only one complete movement, I will divide the lift into two parts to make it easier for explanation.

First, that part of the lift until the feet are moved:

Start the movement with a vigorous legs' drive, taking care

to keep the back straight and not to raise the buttocks before the bar-bell leaves the platform. Many lifters do raise the buttocks before the bar-bell is moved and this means that there is some loss of power from the legs' drive. A conscious effort to start the lift by leading upwards with the head and shoulders helps to counteract this fault. If the bar-bell leaves the platform simultaneously with the first upwards movement of the buttocks, then that is ideal. It is important at this stage to maintain a straight back in order to obtain the maximum combined strength of legs and back power. I recommend inhaling as the start of the lift is made.

The bar-bell should be lifted in a movement as vertical as possible with the arms beginning to bend as the bar-bell passes just above knees' height. As the pull is continued the elbows should be extended outwards and upwards to the maximum extent.

As the bar-bell passes the height of the hips, thrust the hips forwards a few inches. This movement will facilitate the correct lowering of the body as it moves downwards to enable the legs to be split and the weight fixed correctly overhead.

Pull the bar-bell as high as possible before the feet are moved into the split position. Gain maximum height by rising on the toes, with the legs fully extended.

It is essential to make an even pull, so that the bar-bell does not travel to either one side or the other. Ensure this by pulling evenly on both legs until the feet are moved.

The tendency among practically all lifters is to move first the leg that is to be placed backwards. Fight this tendency by aiming to get maximum height of pull and concentrating on moving both feet simultaneously.

Premature movement of the rear foot will mean that the final stage of the pull will be made on one leg and, apart from loss of power, the bar-bell will most likely be fixed overhead to one side and not in a properly-balanced position.

If such a fault is only slight, the lift can often be saved by a quick adjustment of the front foot. On the other hand, a very marked sideways movement usually results in the lift being lost, as the bar-bell will be fixed to one side and be well off balance.

The second phase of the complete snatch is the movement

from the maximum pull, with the bar-bell at chest height. At this stage the legs are moved – one forwards, one backwards.

There is, of course, no distinct second movement ; the whole lift must be smooth and continuous. As the bar-bell reaches the height when the leg movement starts there should be no hesitation ; the body must be moved into the split position with all possible speed, at the same time continuing the upwards pull of the bar-bell.

To fix the bar-bell overhead in a balanced, strong and safe position, the body must be lowered to arrive at a position where the trunk is upright, arms stretched upwards vertically, with the bar-bell held over a line passing straight downwards through the shoulders and hips.

The feet should be well apart, the front leg bent at the knee as far as possible, with the knee well forward of the toes. The rear leg should be bent slightly at the knee, stretched well back, with only the toes of the near foot touching the platform. See Plate 25.

The actual lowering of the body starts almost immediately after the feet have started to move.

At this stage, the upwards pull of the arms will be exhausted and as the body starts to lower, the head will be coming down rapidly towards the bar-bell and the wrists must start to turn so that the arms are in a position to be thrust upwards to reach a locked position.

The rules say that the wrists must not turn until the bar-bell has cleared the line of the top of the head. This is one very good reason why the bar-bell must be pulled *high* before this wrist turn movement starts – otherwise, there will be a premature turning of the wrists leading to disqualification.

The legs must be moved directly forwards and backwards ; that is, one leg straight forward from its starting position, the other directly backwards. Avoid at all costs any tendency to bring the feet in together on one line as if walking on a tightrope. Such a position when handling a heavy poundage means that there will not be a broad enough base to balance the weight overhead in a stable position, and the lift will most likely be lost to either one side or the other.

The rear foot will touch the platform before the front one because of the limited range of backward movement of the rear leg as compared with the front one. This will actually benefit the lifter if he thrusts forward from the rear foot as it lands, making it easier to place the front foot sufficiently forward to enable the hips to keep vertically under the shoulders.

As soon as you feel the front foot land on the platform, force the front knee forward so that it goes past the toes (the distance varying according to the mobility of the performer) and the rear heel backward to avoid too much bending of the rear knee – which must at all costs be kept clear of the platform.

As the final split position is reached, look straight forward with the head held erect. Don't drop the head to look down, or throw the head backwards. Either of these movements can throw the line of the trunk out of the upright position which is so essential to keep the hips underneath the shoulders and the upstretched hands.

Unless the body is correctly positioned under the bar-bell there is every possibility of losing a heavy lift. The hips *must* move forwards to come directly under the shoulders.

To recover to the upright and concluding position, first straighten both legs before any foot movement is made. This will bring you to a safe and strong position, from which the final recovery can be made by moving either foot towards the other.

Bring the feet on to a level plane and maintain your concentration on keeping the arms locked until the referee's signal is given.

Squat Method

The squat style of snatching is being used by an increasing number of performers and while there is, generally, a larger proportion of failures among squat snatchers, the style does offer greater poundage possibilities for those who are physically suited to it.

The number of failures is higher because the squat style is more precarious than the split style, in which the mechanical position of the body makes it a little easier to control the lift, and offers a greater chance to save a lift that is not fixed overhead in a perfect position.

The squat style requires a more delicate sense of balance – not found in every lifter – and also a good degree of mobility in the shoulders, according to which variation of style is used.

Many performers use a fairly upright style of snatching, with the hips only a little way behind the shoulders in the low squat position. Others use a more forward inclination of the trunk, with the hips correspondingly farther behind the shoulders. In this style, the shoulders need to be very supple in order to allow the arms to be taken back to compensate for the forward inclination of the trunk.

My own preference is for the trunk to be inclined forward so that the hips are about a foot behind the shoulders. This is a position approximately midway between the almost upright position and the extreme inclined trunk angle. But, of course, a lot depends on the individual. Not everyone can adopt a position where the trunk is inclined forward at a steepish angle – and many are forced to adopt a more upright position.

One disadvantage of using the upright style is that often there is a slowing down of the movement after the wrists have turned, which can easily result in 'pressing out' the bar-bell. In the trunk forward style – when the shoulders and head are deliberately forced downwards away from the bar-bell as the wrists turn over – a snappy straightening of the arms is facilitated, which lessens any possibility of disqualification for 'press out'.

Also the mechanical position is not good, inasmuch that as the line of balance (centre of gravity) can so easily fall behind or in front of the heels, there is only a slight margin for any body sway or manoeuvre if necessary to save the bar-bell from falling out of control.

In the trunk forward style it is easier to make any adjustment if the bar-bell isn't initially fixed overhead correctly.

When using the squat style there is no time taken in disposing the feet – as in the split style – which means that the body can be lowered under the bar-bell more quickly. This does afford a greater poundage potential, allowing less time for the bar-bell to start falling back, as it naturally will if the body is slow in adopting the low squat position.

In the starting position for the split-style Snatch the feet are placed relatively close together, but for the squat style they should be placed wider. About 18–20 in. is a suitable distance.

Again the bar-bell should be pulled up close to the body, in a vertical line – up to approximately the height of the nipples – before lowering the body and thrusting the arms to a straightened position.

Some lifters like to make a slight forward feet movement, jumping the feet clear of the platform. Experiments can be made with the method. It may be found to suit some lifters, but not all, by any means.

In order to take full advantage of this style the squat should be as full as possible, turning the knees out, more so if an upright style is being used. With the bar-bell fixed safely overhead, the recovery presents no difficulty.

In the event of the line of balance being either too far forward or backward, the head and shoulders can be used to make the necessary adjustment.

With the bar-bell in front of the line of balance, the head and shoulders should be dropped forward and downward. With the bar-bell behind the line of balance, the head should be raised and the shoulders brought back a little. Usually the adjustment will be slight, unless a very bad lift is made.

Adjustment can also be made by rocking either forward or backward slightly on the heels, thus taking the hips either forward or backward. Consistent practice over a period will give a lifter the 'feel' of the movement and his own particular best way of adjusting his balance.

It is necessary, to achieve the best results from squat snatching, to build great strength in the legs, more so than when the split style is used. Hints on building up this strength are given in a later chapter.

CHAPTER EIGHTEEN

How to perform the Two Hands Clean and Jerk

THE Clean and Jerk is really two lifts in one, and as such – coupled with the fact that it is the lift in which the heaviest poundage can be handled – it is a supreme test of all the qualities of a strength athlete.

It is important, too, in this respect: it is the final and deciding lift of a competition. A competitor who is placed behind his rivals on the Press and Snatch can often win by a last supreme effort on the Clean and Jerk.

As with the Snatch, two styles are favoured – the split and the squat; although in all cases the split style is used for the jerk part of the lift.

Main advantages of the squat style are that (a) the technical movements are easier on the clean and (b) the bar-bell does not have to be pulled quite so high before the body is lowered into the squat position. These are great advantages if one has the essential leg strength to use this style.

I will deal with the split style first. The commencing stance is exactly the same as described earlier for the Press.

The grip used for the Press and Snatch is not, for most lifters, of vital importance – owing to the comparatively light weight being handled – but in the Clean and Jerk it is essential that the strongest-possible grip be used to facilitate the pull of the bar-bell to the necessary minimum height before moving into the split position.

On the Clean and Jerk, most lifters handle anything between 50 and 100 lb. more than in the Press and Snatch, and any weakness of grip will mean that their potential on the lift will be cut down.

For some lifters the normal handgrip may be adequate, but many find they need to use the hook grip in order to reach their maximum potential.

The width of the handgrip should approximate that of the Press – about shoulders' width, generally.

But I suggest that a few variations of grip be tried, especially in the case of lifters who find it difficult to hold their weights overhead comfortably because of tight shoulder articulations or a bad arm lock.

In such cases, a slightly wider than normal grip will be more effective ; but not too wide, as for most lifters excessive width will make it more difficult for cleaning.

With some slight differences the same principles of pulling and leg movements advised for the Snatch apply to this lift.

First, the bar-bell doesn't need to be pulled to the same height as in the Snatch before the feet move. Second, the arm movement differs after the feet have started to split and the disposition of the legs is not quite the same.

Start the movement by a vigorous straightening of the legs, maintaining a flat back and bringing in the complete combination of leg drive and arm pull as the bell reaches approximately knees height after being pulled upwards in a vertical line.

Although theoretically it is mechanically sound to pull the bar-bell upwards in a direct vertical line to obtain maximum power it is noticeable that many top-line lifters first pull off the vertical line slightly towards the lower legs, then as the bar-bell passes the height of the knees it is swung outwards again to follow the normal upward path to the shoulders. When using this method the movement of the legs must be slightly different, with the knees being drawn backwards more than in the normal method I have described. Then, following the outwards swing of the bar-bell, the knees are thrust forwards before finally being straightened as the bar-bell approaches waist height.

Beginners should take note of this variation of style of cleaning and later, after a period of training and when more familiar with the technique of the lift, give it a trial.

Pull the bar-bell to about waist height before moving the legs. At this stage, the body should be stretched to full height, head thrust well up – even back a little – legs straight and rising on the toes to get maximum height of pull.

The bar-bell should be close to the body and the hips eased forwards as the bar-bell passes that height. The arms should begin to bend as they continue the strong upwards pull. (See Plate 27.)

Start the splitting of the legs by moving both feet together. As the body begins to lower, the bar-bell will be nearing chest height and should be turned into the shoulders by a backwards movement of the wrists combined with a forward thrust of the elbows.

Bring the bar-bell right up to the top of the sternum bone so that it settles in the base of the throat and ensure that the elbows are thrust forwards with the forearms almost parallel with the floor – the safest possible position for holding the bar-bell.

The feet movement must be directly forwards and backwards as described for the Snatch – although many lifters will be unable to go into quite the same low and wide position.

As the foot lands on the platform push forward with the knee to bring that over the top of the toes, or even farther forward, depending on one's mobility. This will enable the hips to be brought directly under the weight at the shoulders. Keep the chest well up and the head taken back a little. (See Plate 28.)

In order to reach maximum poundages when using the split style of cleaning, the body should be lowered to the fullest extent that the leg strength allows, bearing in mind the necessity of employing a safety margin to avoid any possibility of the knee of the rear leg touching the platform. The rear leg should be only slightly bent at the knee – and a useful tip here to help this is to push backwards with the rear heel as you reach the low split position. This will normally keep the knee off the platform unless, of course, the weight is so heavy that you are forced down too far.

Speed is very important, too. The movement of the legs into the split position should be made with all possible speed. Any undue slowness in this movement with heavy weights will mean failure to complete the movement.

Make the recovery to the erect position without any undue pause – first by almost straightening both legs, then completing the movement by bringing either foot into line with the other.

Breathing

As in the Snatch I advise that the lifter inhales as he makes the effort of pulling. Adopt the starting position, concentrate for a second or two, then start the leg drive simultaneously with the taking of a rapid breath. Your lungs should be full as you reach the clean position. Then, as you rise to the erect position you can exhale, ready to take one or two breaths as you prepare to jerk the bar-bell overhead.

Squat Method

Placing of the feet should be wider than in the split method – about 16–18 in. is a suitable distance.

The first stages of the clean movement are the same as for the split style. This is, the initial leg drive should start the bar-bell moving off the platform and the power of the arms' pull comes in as the legs are approaching the straight position.

Since the mechanics of this movement are simpler, basically all that is required is a strong pull to bring the bar-bell about as high as the line of the hips followed by a quick squat to catch the bar-bell at the chest combined with a turning of the wrists and a thrusting forwards of the elbows.

It is even more essential to thrust the elbows forwards in this style so that they are kept clear of the thighs – any touching of the elbows on the thighs being cause for disqualification.

The depth of the squat will depend on one's leg strength. The deeper and quicker the squat is made the higher becomes the poundage potential. But one needs stronger legs to rise from the full squat position (by full I mean as deep as your mobility will allow). With some lifters this means going so low that the hips are much lower than the knees. Others, particularly the heavier and more solidly-built lifters, find that their lowest position is when the tops of the thighs are parallel with the floor.

The constant practice of squats – both with the bar-bell held at the front of the chest and behind the neck – will build up the necessary leg strength to justify this method of cleaning.

Unless one can do a full front squat with a poundage above one's best clean in the split style there is no point in adopting the squat style.

The Jerk

The commencing position for the jerk should be adopted with the minimum of delay, bringing the feet on to a level plane as required by the rules. I recommend that the bar-bell is held with the elbows and deltoids thrust well forwards to enable it to rest on a solid base across the front of the shoulders.

The body should be held as tall as possible and fairly tensed. Hold this position just sufficiently long enough to prepare yourself mentally for the jerk, taking one or two breaths first.

Power for the jerk must come from a strong and vigorous legs' drive. First, lower the body just a few inches (from 4 to 6) by a bending of the knees so that the bar-bell is lowered *absolutely vertically*, while keeping the heels on the floor.

It is essential to lower the bar-bell vertically so that when the rebound movement is made and the bar-bell is thrust upwards, it moves vertically. If the body is leaned forward in the initial dip, then the bar-bell will almost certainly be thrust forward when jerking as a natural, compensating movement, thus making it necessary to 'chase' the bar-bell by hastily stepping forward farther.

As soon as the maximum depth of the dip is reached, without any pause vigorously restraighten the legs to thrust the bar-bell off the shoulders, rising on the toes to get maximum height before splitting the legs in a fore-and-aft movement similar to the clean part of the lift.

The initial drive from the legs will send the bar-bell moving upwards off the shoulders and it should reach approximately the height of the top of the head before the legs are moved.

From this point the arms should be brought into play with a vigorous thrust to facilitate the drive of the bar-bell to arms' length. As soon as the arms are locked concentrate to keep them so by pressing upwards as hard as possible.

Many lifters look upwards to watch the bar-bell while making the jerk. But I advise the practice of looking almost directly ahead. Looking up at the bar-bell can often lead to a leaning back of the trunk, a position to be avoided.

The bar-bell should be fixed overhead so that a vertical line falls through the head, shoulders and hips, with the legs placed equally fore and aft. Use a moderately wide and low split, not to the same extent as in the Snatch and Clean. Plate 31 shows an ideal position.

Recover to the finishing position as described in the clean, first straightening both legs before moving them in together. Bring both feet on to a level plane, still concentrating to keep your arms locked under the weight. Hold steady for the referee's signal.

CHAPTER NINETEEN

Other recognized lifts

WHILE Olympic weight lifting is the most popular form of the sport – in fact, in many countries the three Olympic lifts are the only recognized movements – the British Amateur Weight Lifters' Association recognizes many other feats. In fact, no less than thirty-one lifts are listed officially for the purposes of record breaking, certificates of merit, and for league and friendly contests. Only a few years ago the number was as high as forty-four.

When I first came into the sport, all-round lifting on a great variety of movements was very popular, even more so than Olympic lifting. But as the trend gradually turned towards Olympic specialization, the number of other feats practised dwindled. This was one reason why the governing body reduced the number of official lifts.

Nowadays the great majority of lifters practise only the Olympic-three, with a gradually increasing number concentrating on the Strength-Set – the Two Hands' Curl, Press on Bench and the Deep Knees Bend. This set is more popular with the body-builder type of weight lifter, as the lifts form a basis for most body-building schedules. In fact, they were introduced into B.A.W.L.A.'s official lifts about eleven years ago to attract more members to the association.

In pre-war days, and for a few years after the war, there were two sets of annual championships held – the Olympic championships and the Amateur championships. As a means of encouraging the all-round performer, and to give more lifters a chance to win a national title, the Amateur championships were held on a different set of lifts each year.

Nowadays – and somewhat regrettably, in my view – the all-rounder receives little or no encouragement at all and, as many of the lifts apart from the Olympics and Strength Set are quite attractive and also very useful for all-round training and enjoyment, I feel that the governing body is wasting an opportunity of presenting to the public a phase of weight lifting that could help to attract more followers and devotees. I am thinking in particular of such lifts as the single-handed Swings, Snatches and Jerks, the Two Hands Continental Jerk, among others.

It has been said by the governing body that as there is little demand for all-round lifting, it is not worth while organizing championships on such lifts. Also that there are few instructors and coaches who have practical knowledge of lifts other than the Olympic and Strength Set lifts.

There is some truth in this but they are problems that could be solved if the will to do it was there. Encouragement *could* be given to the all-round lifter. Instructors *could* be trained in the arts of some of the forgotten lifts.

In the past I have organized many open competitions on various sets of lifts and have always received good support in the way of competitors and audiences, and I am sure that a campaign directed towards encouraging practice of some of the best and most attractive of the other lifts would bring good results in both renewed interest and increased membership.

Here is a complete list of the thirty-one official B.A.W.L.A. lifts:

1. Right Hand Press.
2. Left Hand Press.
3. Right Hand Snatch.
4. Left Hand Snatch.
5. Right Hand Swing.
6. Left Hand Swing.
7. Right Hand Clean and Jerk.
8. Left Hand Clean and Jerk.
9. Right Hand Dead Lift.
10. Left Hand Dead Lift.
11. Rectangular Fix.
12. Lateral Raise Standing.
13. Lateral Raise Lying.
14. Hold Out in Front Raised.
15. Hold Out in Front Lowered.
16. Pull Over at Arms' Length.
17. Pull Over and Press.
18. Two Hands Swing.
19. Two Hands Clean and Press Dumb-bells.
20. Two Hands Clean and Jerk Dumb-bells.

21. Two Hands Anyhow Dumb-bells.
22. Two Hands Curl.
23. Two Hands Clean and Press Bar-bell.
24. Two Hands Snatch.
25. Two Hands Clean and Press from behind Neck.
26. Two Hands Clean and Jerk from behind Neck.
27. Two Hands Clean and Jerk Bar-bell.
28. Two Hands Continental Jerk Bar-bell.
29. Two Hands Dead Lift.
30. Press on Bench.
31. Deep Knees' Bend.

CHAPTER TWENTY

Making a start

LET'S assume you are an average young man of seventeen or so, in good health. You will most likely have been introduced to weight lifting by a friend, have maybe been along to a club or a championship meeting and become interested enough to want to have a go yourself. Perhaps you have already dabbled in some sport or physical activity. If so, this will make things easier for you as you will already possess some degree of physical fitness.

It's hard work

Let me emphasize from the first that competitive weight lifting means hard work except for a few fortunate people who are naturally very strong and athletic and who seem to make rapid progress on a comparatively small amount of training. It is such people who usually become our champions, for it isn't solely the amount and intensity of training that makes a champion. There are thousands of competitive lifters who have trained on sound principles and harder and longer than most of the existing champions, but because they haven't been endowed with sufficient natural ability and potential they still remain only average performers.

In a few instances lifters of low potential and weak natural resources have, by more-than-average determination and stickability, risen to championship standard, but such cases are the exception rather than the rule and even those who are favourably treated by nature have to work hard to become really outstanding performers, so high is the standard these days.

The intensity of a man's training is governed largely by his interest and his ambition, for a man will rarely become a weight-lifting champion unless (a) he really wants to be one, and (b) he pursues his ambition with a relentless determination. In addition, of course, he needs the right encouragement, environment and proper training facilities.

No Short Cut

I have dwelt on these points because I want everyone who intends becoming an Olympic weight lifter to realize fully what is involved. You will have to train, generally, about three times weekly almost all the year round for a long time before you approach your maximum potential.

There are few men like, for example, the late Khadr el Touni (former Egyptian world champion) who pressed 180 lb. the first time he handled a bar-bell at a very young age, or England's Phil Caira, who was pressing 200 lb. at fifteen years, after only a short time at the sport, and former world champion, giant Paul Anderson, who was a natural strength colossus and took to heavy lifting like a duck to water.

The majority of beginners are naturally weak and have a mediocre potential and for this reason many try weight lifting for a time, then give it up. But for those who do stick it, the reward is good, even if they don't become outstanding or champions. The gradual building up of strength and athletic ability has many benefits, mental as well as physical, and the years spent at this sport are most certainly worth while.

Seventeen is about the average age for beginners, but it is not necessarily the best age to start. It depends largely on the individual. Some youngsters are very mature for their years and can safely make a start at fifteen or even earlier. But the earlier the start the more important it is to train only under someone who has had some experience of coaching.

Youngsters are notoriously eager and often want to progress at a rate that is much too fast to be good for them. All beginners need looking after at the start and more so when they are very young.

What the Sport Offers

The progressive principles of competitive weight lifting make it, in my experience, one of the best forms of physical culture. Not only is the muscular system toned and strengthened, but the even more important factor of organic fitness is well looked after. Mental benefits include the development of greater self confidence as physical power is increased. In fact, one's whole outlook on life is greatly improved, a boon particularly to those who are naturally shy and self-conscious.

One of the rewards of being a weight lifter is that it gives a feeling of achievement, together with a physical and mental uplift that has to be experienced to be fully appreciated. It offers the thrill and fun of competition with other sportsmen and the opportunity of achieving some kind of fame. It also provides an activity that brings great physical benefit, developing qualities of strength, speed, agility, balance and courage: qualities that will prove useful in fields other than weight lifting.

There are many opportunities for official recognition for all grades of lifters, including schemes for national, divisional, state and local championships and records, and weight-lifting leagues give an opportunity for everyone to compete and gain experience.

Those who reach a high enough standard can become national champions, and possibly represent their country in such events as international contests, world championships and Olympic Games. Only a few will reach the top, travelling the world and taking part in big events. Most will fall short of their ambitions and potential and remain as ordinary lifters. But however far you travel along the road to fame you will benefit both physically and mentally.

Amateur Status

Olympic weight lifting is, of course, an amateur sport and in order to compete officially you will have to enter an event sanctioned by the official governing body, the Amateur Athletic Union of the U.S.   13700 **Woodward Avenue, Detroit 3, Michigan.**

Briefly, an amateur is one who has never taken part in any sport or physical activity for direct or indirect financial gain, or never competed against a professional. If you are, or have been, a professional at any other sport, then you will be regarded as a professional at weight lifting.

The whole question of amateur status is very complex and one of the most controversial problems of modern international sport. It is not quite so simple as my brief description above, but I do not propose to debate such a delicate subject here. If any reader has doubts about his own status, then this can be settled by contacting the amateur governing body.

CHAPTER TWENTY-ONE

Principles of training

WEIGHT lifting is a demanding sport. It means a lot of hard work over a long time, often interspersed with periods of frustration and staleness when little or no progress is made. The road to the top isn't easy but the journey can be made smoother if the right route is taken. And this means training on the best and most economical principles.

It is true that the method of trial and error has to be applied in some instances: in variation of lifting technique, the number of repetitions to be performed in the various lifts and exercises, frequency of training and so on. Nevertheless, the basic principles of performance and training apply to everyone. It is only in the variations of these principles that individual expression is found. This comes only with experience and a gradual learning of oneself.

In the early stages of one's weight-lifting career it is advisable to follow the accepted patterns, based on long experience.

The most important requirement of an Olympic lifter is unquestionably great strength. Other necessary qualities, such as good lifting technique, the right mental approach, suppleness of limbs and joints, speed of movement, balance, co-ordination and courage, all have a part in the complete make-up, but none rates so high as the possession of great strength.

Every top-line lifter and champion possesses great strength. Some have excellent technique, most have good or reasonable technique and a few of them are champions despite the fact that they lack good technique.

But not one of them reached the top with just moderate strength.

Even with perfect technique no man can lift really heavy or record poundages unless this technique is allied to great strength.

Some of the best technicians I have seen have been in the ranks of club and league lifters, but they have remained in that class because they lacked the power of the world champions. It is true, of course, that many a champion could be an even better champion if he improved his lifting skill, because it is necessary to develop the best-possible technique in order fully to utilize whatever degree of strength one may possess. Yet I know from a long experience that many performers find it difficult to attain good technique. It may be because of some physical disability, such as tight shoulder-articulations, stiffness in the hip and ankle joints ; or it may be that they are naturally slow in their movements and reactions (a virtually essential part of good technique is speed of movement).

Generally, the best technicians are the naturally-athletic types, with good flexibility and quick reactions. Yet even the poorest technicians can improve by perseverance and practice.

On the other hand, I believe that for most lifters it is relatively easier to develop strength than technique, and the equivalent time spent on strength development often gives better results.

Since all lifters are just not capable of developing good, or even near-good technique it can often be a waste of time trying to reach a technical standard that is quite beyond you. To expect *every* Olympic lifter to reach 100 per cent precision and skill is, in my view, asking too much. Attain the highest-possible technical standard, by all means, and maintain this by constant practice, but remember that the ultimate object of training is to improve your *total* on the three lifts, and if it is found that more work on strength building brings higher totals, then be wise and exploit this to the full. However, don't ever neglect technique. It is important – but not by any means the complete answer to higher Olympic totals.

Remember that all of us have only a certain amount of time available for training, and this should be used wisely to get maximum benefit. More time spent on technique work means less time spent on power work, which is the real basis of building the strength necessary to hoist record poundages.

The ideal programme for the advanced man is to adjust his training from time to time, concentrating on that part of his lifting that is lacking at any particular period.

The First Steps

For the beginner it is essential that some reasonable degree of lifting skill and positional efficiency should first be cultivated before attempting to lift heavy weights, and one's early training should be directed to this end.

Many instructors believe that a potential Olympic lifter should first spend a few months working on standard body-building exercises. Others believe that it is preferable to go straight on to the Olympic movements without any preliminary body-building work.

My own view is that this depends largely on the individual. If a pupil is naturally weak and underweight (and the majority generally are) and has never practised physical culture, exercised or played games at all I think it is wise to spend some time on body building and strengthening exercises before going on to learn the more complicated movements of Olympic lifting. But some who wish to start weight lifting have already developed a fair amount of strength and athletic ability, maybe through gymnastics, physical training or games. In such cases, preliminary weight training is not so essential and one could straight away start Olympic-lifts training.

Frequency of Training

As a minimum requirement to make satisfactory progress I consider three sessions weekly are essential. Progress can be made on less work, but generally it will not be enough for the best results. One cannot hope to reach a high standard of performance without hard work and dedication. Even the naturally strong and athletic types, who respond well to normal training and generally make faster progress, need plenty of hard work if they aim to become champions, and the man who does not possess much natural potential, the man whose heredity and physical type handicaps him to some extent from the start, has to work much harder for equivalent gains.

However, guard against overtraining. This is just as bad as not doing enough.

Actually the intensity and quality of training should vary at different periods, depending upon whether there is any particular contest due in the near future or not. One cannot keep in hard training and in tip-top form for an unlimited period. Rather, training should fluctuate, building up and intensifying as a contest approaches, followed by a period of comparative relaxation before starting to build up again.

Normally, with nothing particular in view, one should keep in reasonably good condition with three or four training sessions weekly, working up to limit or near-limit poundages about once a fortnight – except perhaps on the Press, when limit attempts may be tackled more frequently.

Then, as the contest approaches, the work done can be stepped up to bring peak condition. After the contest, it is wise to rest completely for a few days, then start a building-up process again, bearing in mind that many weight lifters lift limit weights in competition largely with the aid of severe mental concentration. And in order not to tax the nervous system too much, one must take periods of relaxation.

Repetitions and Poundages

To develop any physical quality, one's training must consist largely of similar movements and exertions.

Weight lifting is a sport that demands short and sharp explosive efforts, interspersed with brief rest periods. The quality of stamina – as employed in such activities as track athletics, swimming, cycling, for example – is not required. Stamina of a kind is necessary, but of a totally different nature.

Training for Olympic weight lifting must be directed towards developing the quality of being able to concentrate one's energies and mental concentration for this brief explosion of power.

High repetitions will not develop this power to maximum extent, but will tend to develop the quality of being able to perform high repetitions, and to increase muscular size rather than strength.

Low repetitions (generally threes, twos and single lifts) are essential for the development of the essential qualities required – *with heavy weights.*

In weight-lifting competition, only three attempts are allowed on any one lift – all with limit and near-limit poundages.

Your training schedules should be designed so that most of the time devoted to the actual Olympic movements is spent in lifting poundages that are approaching your limits.

There is room for occasional periods of training with light weights – apart from normal warming up, which should be used in every training session – as a means of avoiding possible staleness and boredom, and for training on technique work and developing extra speed when it is felt that such diversity of training is needed.

Detailed schedules based on these principles are given in Chapter Twenty-two.

Other Activities

When one is specializing on Olympic weight lifting, there is little time left for participating in other physical activities. Furthermore, additional activity can lessen one's chances of making maximum progress at weight lifting – unless it is of a limited nature and deliberately designed to help your progress at weight lifting.

Such activities as a little handbalancing (for improving your Press when special balancing movements are concentrated on) or gymnastics to improve balance and co-ordination, are very useful. But make sure not to overdo anything of this nature.

One of the finest activities, and one which I really consider essential as an aid to greater efficiency, is running – the oldest, cheapest, the most natural, and perhaps the best fitness producer ever known.

Yes, running should be included in your training programme. Get out on the road once or twice a week, jog-trotting, or alternately running and fast walking, and you will soon get that extra edge on your condition that cannot fail to help you.

There is no need to rush at it. Start off with a medium jog of about a mile for a few nights. Then gradually build up until you do three or four miles.

Think for Yourself

Each individual has to decide his own destiny. He will have certain interests and ambitions in the sport. He will have a quota of natural potential, which will help him to a degree dependent on its quality. To this, a basis for progress, will have to be added plenty of hard work and dedication.

From then on, he is master of his fate. The man who forges ahead of the others will be the one who applies these qualities with the greatest force and wisdom.

Although a book of this nature can help to make the journey through the beginner's stage easier, one must all the time be thinking and acting on personal experience and progress. I have no quarrel at all with anyone who departs from the orthodox path if he finds he can make greater progress that way. Indeed I applaud him. Many champions in sport are men who have decided that their own way is best, but generally, this departure from the accepted path should not be made until one has first followed the normal pattern of technique and training methods.

CHAPTER TWENTY-TWO

Schedules for the beginner

THE character of a training schedule on the Olympic lifts is dependent on a combination of repetitions of each movement, the number of sets, the poundage employed and frequency of training.

Low repetitions with heavy weights is the proved best route to maximum strength and efficiency – but a beginner, in his first months of training, should use higher repetitions with correspondingly lighter weights.

This is because a beginner's muscular system isn't fully toned and accustomed to handling heavy poundages – and I believe that a gradual building-up process should be followed right from the start, even although one may have undergone a period of body-building with weights before starting on Olympic lifting.

The use of light weights – gradually progressing to heavier ones – is the best method of accustoming the muscles to the technical movements required, particularly on the Snatch and Clean and Jerk.

It is important to avoid the use of heavy weights while learning these movements. Later, the weight used can be stepped up and the number of repetitions reduced.

Generally, I recommend that this type of schedule be employed for a period of at least three months – and longer in the case of individuals who are not naturally athletic, supple and speedy.

Here are some typical schedules that will serve the two-fold purpose of enabling the movements to be learned without having to force oneself too much to handle heavy weights, and at the same time giving sufficient resistance to gradually build up strength.

TWO HANDS PRESS

The weight used, of course, will vary according to one's strength and bodyweight, but I will base this on an assumed ability of 120 lb. for one strict movement. Adjustments can then be made according to ability.

85 lb.	5	repetitions	2	sets
95 lb.	4	repetitions	2	sets
100 lb.	3	repetitions	3	sets
105 lb.	2	repetitions	3	sets
85 lb.	6	repetitions	1	set

Fixed-poundage Schedule

As an alternative, use the following:

95 lb.	4	repetitions	7	sets

Once a fortnight, work up to a maximum poundage on the following lines:

85 lb.	3	repetitions	2	sets
95 lb.	3	repetitions	2	sets
100 lb.	3	repetitions	1	set
110 lb.	2	repetitions	1	set
115 lb.	1	single lift		
120 lb.	1	single lift		

Then try 125 lb. in order to achieve a new maximum poundage.

All repetitions are to be made from the shoulders, performed in strict competition style.

Two Hands Snatch

Repetitions and poundages are base on an assumed ability of 120 lb. for one strict movement.

85 lb.	4	repetitions	2	sets
95 lb.	4	repetitions	2	sets
100 lb.	3	repetitions	2	sets
105 lb.	2	repetitions	2	sets

Fixed-poundage Schedule

As an alternative, try the following:

100 lb.	4	repetitions	5	sets

Once a fortnight, work up to a maximum poundage on the following lines:

85 lb.	3	repetitions	2	sets
95 lb.	3	repetitions	2	sets
100 lb.	3	repetitions	1	set
110 lb.	2	repetitions	1	set

115 lb.   1 single lift
120 lb.   1 single lift

Then try 125 lb. in order to achieve a new maximum poundage.

Repetitions are to be made from the commencing position each time. Make your first lift, then lower the bar-bell to the floor, reassume the commencing position immediately, pause just a second or two, then repeat the lift.

Two Hands Clean and Jerk

Repetitions and poundages are based on an assumed ability of 150 lb. for one strict movement.

On this lift, it is advisable to regard the Clean and the Jerk as two separate lifts for the bulk of your training, although some time must be spent performing the complete movement.

110 lb.   3 cleans   2 sets
120 lb.   2 cleans   2 sets
130 lb.   2 cleans   2 sets
110 lb.   3 jerks   2 sets
120 lb.   2 jerks   2 sets
130 lb.   2 jerks   2 sets

Then: 120 lb.   2 cleans and 1 jerk.   2 sets

When performing the Clean, make your repetitions in the same way as the Snatch, replacing the bar-bell on the floor before making the next repetition. On the Jerk, make your repetitions consecutive from the shoulders, as in the Press.

Fixed-poundage Schedule

As an alternative, use the following:

120 lb.   3 cleans   5 sets
          3 jerks   5 sets

Once a fortnight, work up to a maximum complete lift on the following lines:

110 lb.   2 cleans   2 sets
          2 jerks   2 sets
120 lb.   2 cleans   1 set
          2 jerks   1 set
130 lb.   1 complete lift
140 lb.   1 complete lift

145 lb. 1 complete lift
150 lb. 1 complete lift

Then try 155 lb. in order to achieve a new maximum poundage.

When trying the extra 5 lb. on your limits, as specified above, add another 5 lb. if successful, until a new absolute maximum is reached. Then, add weight to all your poundages for the various repetitions and sets, to make your work progressive.

SUPPLEMENTARY EXERCISES

Even at this early stage it is advisable to include a few supplementary exercises in the schedule, and I suggest the following:

Squat (full movement)

110 lb. 6 repetitions 2 sets
120 lb. 5 repetitions 2 sets
130 lb. 4 repetitions 2 sets

Use the following fixed-poundage schedule as an alternative:

120 lb. 5 repetitions 6 sets

Power Clean

100 lb. 4 repetitions 2 sets
110 lb. 4 repetitions 2 sets
120 lb. 3 repetitions 2 sets
130 lb. 2 repetitions 2 sets

Use the following fixed-poundage schedule as an alternative:

120 lb. 4 repetitions 6 sets

Bench Press

110 lb. 4 repetitions 2 sets
120 lb. 4 repetitions 2 sets
130 lb. 3 repetitions 2 sets
140 lb. 2 repetitions 2 sets

Use the following fixed-poundage schedule as an alternative:

130 lb. 4 repetitions 6 sets

The poundages for the supplementary exercises may have to be adjusted according to one's ability.

If one is able to train four times weekly, I suggest that on two days the Olympic lifts only should be practised and on the other two days, two of the lifts plus the supplementary exercises.

Thus, your training programme would read like this:

Monday: Olympic lifts only.

Wednesday: Press and Snatch, plus supplementary exercises.

Friday: Olympic lifts only.

Saturday or Sunday: Press and Jerk, plus supplementary exercises.

I advise this type of programme, because generally, the practice of the Olympic lifts and all the supplementary exercises in one session will be rather too much for many beginners and will probably occupy too much time.

If you find that the three lifts and exercises can be managed comfortably and without any after-effects of fatigue, then by all means do them, but usually it is not wise for a beginner to force himself during the first few months of training. After this period, you will be able to make a self-assessment of capacity for work, the muscular system will be getting used to the effects of the training and the amount of work undertaken can be increased accordingly.

Many will not find it possible to devote four sessions to training, and if this is the case, the above programme will need adjustment according to individual circumstances and physical capacity.

CHAPTER TWENTY-THREE

Advanced training and assistance exercises

Building Great Strength

The first few months of training on the beginners' schedule will have brought noticeable gains in both technique and strength.

Now it is time to move on to something of a more advanced nature, making a gradual change over to heavier poundages in lower repetitions and incorporating more power building exercises into your schedules. The quest for greater and greater strength must be the major and constant aim of the ambitious Olympic weight lifter.

The practice of the Olympic lifts themselves will develop greater strength, but I do not believe that one's maximum strength potential can be reached by training solely on the three Olympic movements. Eventually there will be a limit to progress and for maximum results one must include other exercises in the training programme to give added boost.

Experience of the world's greatest lifters supports this contention. All of them use a wide variety of other exercises to build maximum strength.

Generally the best movements are those which work the largest and strongest muscle groups and movements similar to the Olympic lifts in which greater weights can be handled.

Here is a selection of the best strength-building and assistance exercises:

The Squat

One of the finest of all strength-building movements is the Squat, or Deep Knees Bend.

The legs play a major part in the Snatch and Clean and Jerk, particularly when using the squat style of lifting. And regular, progressive practice of the Squat is recognized as one of the greatest of all power builders.

All the great strong men – past and present – have used Squat as the key movement in building power.

The best method is to practise half and quarter Squats – both with the weight held behind the shoulders and in front.

You will need plenty of weight – as in these partial movements a lot can be handled. The full Squat shouldn't be neglected, of course, especially for those lifters who use the squat style for the Clean and the Snatch, but for real power you need to use half and quarter squats, performed with as much weight as you can handle in sets of low repetitions.

You will need to use squat stands. Make sure that they are strong and solid. If you train at a club, you will most likely find it equipped with suitable stands. If at home, ensure that your stands are safe and in a convenient position in your room. You will be handling very heavy poundages and must ensure safety at all times.

Here is a suitable squatting programme:

Warm up with one set of full Squats with a moderate poundage – from 7 to 10 repetitions. Rest a few moments, then load up to a poundage in excess of your best Clean and Jerk.

Perform 6 repetitions, squatting to a point where the top of the thighs are parallel with the floor. Lower steadily and without hesitation, resisting the weight to avoid a too-rapid descent. As soon as the parallel positon is reached, return to the starting position. Take one or two deep breaths, then repeat until your repetitions are complete.

In order to ensure that the legs are doing the major part of the work, keep the back as flat and as upright as possible, with the head held up.

Repeat 6 repetitions after a breather.

Now add 20 lb. and perform 5 repetitions for 2 sets.

Add another 20 lb. and perform 4 repetitions for 2 sets.

Take a breather now for four or five minutes, but make sure to keep warm.

Add another 20 lb. and perform 6 repetitions of the quarter Squat – that is, lowering to a point midway between the upright position and the half Squat position.

Add another 20 lb. and perform 5 repetitions to complete the schedule.

Bench Press

Many of the world's greatest Olympic pressers use the Bench

Press as a supplementary exercise and have obtained great benefit from it.

In the competition Bench Press, a fairly-wide handgrip is generally used. But when using this movement as an aid to Olympic lifting, it is advisable to use the same width grip as that for the Olympic Press – approximately shoulders' width. A description of the movement is given in Chapter Six.

If you have access to a bench fitted with stands for this movement you will avoid having to use two assistants to hand you the weight each time.

Here is a useful schedule:

Warm up with one set of 8 repetitions with a moderate poundage – approximately 10–20 lb. less than your best Olympic Press.

Add 20–30 lb. and perform 5 repetitions. Repeat another 5 repetitions.

Add 10 lb. and perform 4 repetitions. Repeat another 4 repetitions.

Add 10 lb. and perform 3 repetitions. Repeat another 3 repetitions.

Do not bounce the bar-bell off the chest each time. Lower steadily to touch the chest in the region of the nipples, hold for one second, then press vigorously and steadily to full locked arms.

If you have an inclined bench available, practise the press on this as a variation, using different angles from time to time.

As another variation, the press can be performed with two dumb-bells.

High Pulls

The ability to pull heavy weights high and fast is one of the greatest assets of an Olympic lifter. And constant and regular practice of high pulling movements is a MUST in order to develop fully this essential quality.

The high pull as an assistance movement for the Clean and Jerk resembles a fast Dead Lift, but with the weight pulled higher – to at least the level of the waistline.

Use the same width grip as for the Clean and Jerk and start the movement in exactly same way. Pull up the weight fast to waist level, rising on the toes and thrusting the hips forward as the bar-bell approaches waist height. Keep the head well up.

Lower bar-bell to the floor, resume starting position and repeat.

Warm up with a weight about 40 lb. less than your best Clean, and perform 6 repetitions.

Add 20 lb. and perform 4 repetitions. Repeat 4 repetitions.

Add 20 lb. and perform 3 repetitions. Repeat 3 repetitions.

Add 10 lb. and perform 2 repetitions. Repeat 2 repetitions.

The high pull as an aid to the Snatch should be performed in a similar way, using the same width grip as in the Snatch.

Pull the bell as high as possible towards the chest, keeping the elbows well up and rising on toes to get maximum height.

Poundages, repetitions and sets should be employed on the same basis as above.

When performing the high pulls, it will be found that the strength of your grip is often a deciding factor as to the weight and repetitions handled – and it is advisable to use the much stronger hook grip.

Some lifters use wrist straps to ease the tension on the grip. This enables them to handle heavier poundages.

This strap is usually made of webbing or similar strong material, is wound round the bar-bell and then tightly round the wrists.

Jerk-Press

A useful aid to the Olympic Press, in which the first stage of the Press is started similarly to the Olympic Jerk, lowering the bar-bell by a dip of the legs, then vigorously re-straightening them to thrust the bar-bell off the shoulders.

The leg drive will take the weight to just above eyes' level as the legs straighten – with little assistance from the pressing muscles – and from that position the bar-bell is pressed to full arms' length with the legs braced.

Here is a suitable schedule:

Warm up with a poundage about 30 lb. below your best Press.

Add 20 lb. and perform 4 repetitions. Repeat 4 repetitions.

Add 20 lb. and perform 3 repetitions. Repeat 3 repetitions.

Add 10 lb. and perform 2 repetitions. Repeat 2 repetitions.

Dead Lift

One of the best tests of bodily strength and the movement in which the greatest weight can be lifted.

Regular practice will strengthen the back, thighs and grip, essential for the development of greater Olympic-lifts power.

High pulls, described earlier, are the nearest approach to the Olympic cleaning movement, without actually moving into the split or squat position – and the fact that the bar-bell is pulled to waist height cuts down on the poundage that can be handled.

In the Dead Lift the bar-bell isn't lifted any higher than the position in which the trunk is erect, legs braced and the bar-bell held on locked arms, lying across the thighs.

Use the same width handgrip and the same feet spacing as for the Clean and Jerk. Grasp the bar-bell with a reverse hand-grip – one hand with knuckles to the front, the other with knuckles to the rear.

Keep the back as straight as possible and pull the bar-bell up in a steady, continuous pull to the erect position, using the full power of the legs to start the movement.

Warm up with a weight that can be handled comfortably for 6 repetitions – approximately 50–60 lb. more than your best Clean – replacing the bar-bell on the floor each time, adjusting your body to the correct starting position, pausing just a second or so, then repeating the lift.

Add 50 lb. and perform 4 repetitions. Rest, then repeat 4 repetitions.

Add 20 lb. and perform 2 repetitions. Rest, then repeat 2 repetitions.

Occasionally – about every three or four weeks – work up to a limit poundage, starting with about 80–100 lb. above your best Clean and Jerk and perform 3 repetitions. Add 20 lb. for 2 repetitions, then go up in 20-lb. stages for two or three single lifts, then 10-lb. stages in single lifts until your limit is reached.

Power Clean and Jerk

One of the most popular and effective training movements is cleaning and jerking without any feet movement.

Clean the bar-bell, using just a shallow dip of the body to

receive the weight at the shoulders. Make full use of the legs' drive to start the cleaning movement, which should be speeded up by strong pulling power from the arms.

Straighten up and assume the starting position for the jerk as described in Chapter Seven. To perform the power jerk, start as for the Clean and Jerk proper by making a preliminary dip of the body, lowering about 4 in. or so, then vigorously straightening the legs to thrust the bar-bell upwards from the shoulders. Facilitate this thrust by bringing in the power of the arms.

As the bar-bell nears arms' length quickly bend the legs again to enable the body to be lowered under the weight as the arms lock.

The movement is a partial jerk – as distinct from the power press, in which the weight is pressed to locked arms after the initial leg thrust.

Here is a suitable schedule:

Warm up with a poundage about 10–20 lb. below your best Press. Perform 4 cleans first, replacing the bar-bell on the floor after each repetition. Then perform 4 power jerks from the shoulders.

Add 20 lb. and perform 3 cleans as before. Then 3 power jerks from the shoulders.

Add 10 lb. and perform 2 cleans as before. Then 2 power jerks from the shoulders.

Add 10 lb. and perform 5 single complete lifts. This poundage should be approximately 10–20 lb. below your limit. If felt to be well within your power, add further weight so that a good amount of effort is put into these final single lifts.

Seated Press

In the ordinary Olympic Press, a lot of the work is done by the bracing and supporting muscles of the thighs, buttocks and back.

Pressing in the seated position prohibits the use of the thighs and buttocks and puts more direct stress on the pressing muscles of the deltoids and triceps.

Stand just in front of a chair or bench with the bar-bell on the floor close up in front of you. Clean the bar-bell and immediately sit down. Place your feet in the best position to stabilize you and to minimize the possibility of overbalancing during the pressing movement.

Warm up with a poundage about 50 lb. below your best standing Press and perform 5 repetitions.

Add 10 lb. and perform 3 repetitions. Rest and repeat 3 repetitions.

Add 10 lb. and perform 2 repetitions. Rest and repeat 4 sets of 2 repetitions.

Leg Press

A leg-press machine is the ideal apparatus to use for this movement – but not many clubs possess them. Such a machine can be constructed in various ways.

The best ones usually have a square or rectangular platform that slides up and down in a steel framework. The trainee takes up his position underneath, lying on his back with his feet under the platform, which is loaded with weights.

The platform can be lowered only so far as a safety point, at a height so that the trainee can get his feet underneath with his legs doubled up ready to press the weight upwards until his legs are straightened. It is best to have the buttocks raised a little when performing the movement, resting them on a cushion or something similar – unless you are using a machine that already has something built in to allow the trainee to adopt a position with raised buttocks.

Very heavy weights can be used in this movement – 500 lb. and upwards in many instances.

If a machine is not available, one can perform the leg-pressing movement by balancing a bar-bell on the soles of the feet, which should be approximately hips' width apart. Good, strong heels are essential to avoid the possibility of the bar-bell slipping off the feet. Care must be taken, too, that the bar-bell is kept even, not allowing one end to dip lower than the other. Assistants are necessary to place the bar-bell on the feet and standing by ready to take the bar-bell immediately if necessary.

Practising the leg press in this way demands a very good sense of balance and plenty of confidence. Personally, I have never used a leg-press machine (never having the facilities) but have used the leg press with the bar-bell on feet without any difficulty at all.

It is wise to practise first with a very light weight until a reasonable sense of balance is achieved.

The movement is similar to a Press on bench or back, but using the legs instead of the arms.

Warm up with 8 to 10 repetitions with moderate poundage, then step up the weight and perform several sets of 6 repetitions.

Once you are used to the movement you will find that weight can be added fairly often and you will soon be using several hundred pounds if you practise on a proper leg-press machine.

Using the method of balancing the bar-bell on your feet will, of course, cut down the poundage considerably, but you will still get invaluable results from this movement.

Snatching and Cleaning from Chairs

A very effective exercise for improving the Snatch and Clean is to practise the lifts with the ends of the bar-bell resting on two chairs or benches about knees' height.

Stand close up to the bar-bell so that the knees are almost touching it, take a normal grip and snatch or clean from this position.

This movement helps to build up that important part of the pull from knees' height to the position when the legs are moved into the split or squat, with the bar-bell approximately at chest height. Also, this movement is useful in forcing you to split in a very low position – particularly helpful to those lifters who either from lack of confidence or complete joint mobility do not normally lower the body to a sufficient depth.

Warm up with a light-to-moderate poundage, replacing the bar-bell on the chairs after each repetition. Then perform 4 sets of 2 repetitions, and finally 6 single lifts with a poundage that you can just manage.

Balance and Strength Builders

Other excellent movements designed to give a better sense of balance in the Snatch and Clean are as follows:

For the Snatch, start from a position where a split Snatch has been made – with the bar-bell held overhead. From this position come straight upwards, fully straightening both legs, but do not move the feet. Hold this position for a second or two, then lower again to the low split position. Come straight up again and carry on your repetitions in this manner.

Use a similar movement in the split position for the Clean. This is even more effective as a strength builder, owing to the heavier weight handled. It is, in effect, a form of squat, with the added advantage that the leg muscles are exercised through the exact range of the clean movement.

From the low clean position, straighten the legs so that you rise with the bar-bell as high as possible, then lower again to the split position. With heavy weights it will be advisable – and, in fact, necessary when the weight approaches or exceeds your limit clean – to take the weight off stands, or have it handed in to you by training partners.

In both these movements, warm up first with 5 or 6 repetitions with a light weight. Then add weight and perform 3 sets of 3 repetitions, finally doing 4 sets of 2 repetitions.

Both movements will give greater confidence in splitting very low, plus the necessary power to rise from the low split position without undue difficulty when performing the Snatch and Clean in competition.

These strength-building movements should be incorporated into your programme as convenient, perhaps using three or four of them after working out on the three Olympic lifts – or, at times, dropping the Olympics for a period and using 5 or 6 of the power movements.

Aim to balance your training by concentrating on adjusting any weakness that shows up in your competition performances.

If speed and technique is lacking, work on the Olympic movements exclusively, performing plenty of single lifts with moderate-to-heavy poundages after first warming up with light weights.

When you feel more solid power is needed, then work on the power movements, with just an occasional training spell on the Olympics.

Bodyweight Control

It is inevitable that many lifters will have bodyweight problems, as there are bound to be plenty whose normal bodyweight falls midway between the limits of two classweights. Thus, a man weighing normally 156 pounds is too heavy for a lightweight and too light to get the best out of himself as a middleweight.

He might be able to reduce to the lightweight limit of 148¾ lb., but will most likely lose an appreciable amount of strength and stamina. In this case, the wisest course is to build up the full middleweight limit, using plenty of the heavy exercises and adopting a weight-gaining diet.

Anyone whose normal bodyweight is just two or three pounds above a classweight limit probably won't have any great difficulty in reducing to the limit for competition.

When making such a reduction, slightly reduce the normal diet two or three days before the contest, particularly liquids, watching your weight each day so that too much reduction is not made.

If you are within a pound of the bodyweight limit on the day before the contest there will not, normally, be much to worry about. Take no liquid on the day of the event until the weigh-in.

The lighter men – bantamweights and featherweights – will naturally find it harder to reduce than the heavier men. Sometimes, losing a pound or so can be a difficult task for a man weighing only about 124 lb., especially if he has little surplus fat and has perhaps already reduced a few pounds in the few days before a contest.

This might mean some last-minute reduction by vigorous exercise if still above the bodyweight limit just before the weigh-in. Fast skipping, wearing some very warm clothing, is useful, also vigorous massage of the more fleshy parts of the body.

The whole question of bodyweight reduction without losing strength if possible, is largely a matter for the individual to watch himself by experiment and experience.

If it is found to be constantly difficult to reduce, then I advise building up to the next classweight, particularly in the case of older men, when constant reduction made with difficulty can eventually be a threat to health.

CHAPTER TWENTY-FOUR

Competition hints

COMPETITION is the life-blood of any sport. Without competition, and the incentives that go with it, no one can realize his full potential. One can, of course, practise competitive weight lifting primarily for enjoyment and the physical and mental benefits, but without the opportunity of pitting oneself against the strength and skill of others, it may be difficult to maintain interest over a long period and to reach the heights of what one is capable.

A true champion is a man who revels in competing against his rivals and who produces his best under the stress and incentive of competition. And it is this driving force that often enables a man to win against opposition that, while potentially greater, fails because of a lack of the essential qualities for success.

Many weight lifters consistently leave their best performances in the training room. For some reason or other they fail to reproduce on the competition platform what they have accomplished in training. Largely this is a matter of mental attitude. For example, there is no logical reason why a man who has been pressing, say 200 lb. with some degree of consistency in training, should not succeed with this poundage – or even more – in competition.

I am talking now of the lifter who has some experience behind him. The beginner, obviously, cannot reasonably be expected to exceed his training performances right away in competition; although many will, of course. But the experienced man should and if he finds that he doesn't, then his mental attitude needs overhauling.

Consider these facts:

Training, generally, isn't conducted in the best atmosphere for maximum performances. Usually there is no incentive in the way of competition stimulus, no audience to respond to, no extreme urge to equal or exceed one's previous best. But in competition, all these factors should bring out the full current potential of the performer.

It is not uncommon for good competitors to exceed by 10 or 20 lb. their best training Clean and Jerk when competing in a championship. Many make their best training performance a *starting* poundage in competition – then go on to add anything up to 20 lb. on top of this. And that's how it should be.

If one finds, through experience, that training performances cannot be bettered in competition, then a different attitude of mind must be cultivated. One must think on more positive lines, must deliberately and determinedly set out to develop a better competitive spirit.

This is largely a mental problem and only by continually building up an urge to do better, a positive-thinking attitude to competition, can such improvement be effected. There must be no mental barrier ; no poundage that one sets as a definite limit.

Training can be said to be the most important part of competitive weight lifting. For what is accomplished in competition depends largely on what one does in training. Intelligent preparation for a championship or contest is the basis of efficient performance on the competition platform.

The cultivation of good technique, the building up of more and more bodily power and fitness and conditional training, are all essential steps towards the climax of expression on the platform, but a competitor in any sport must be obsessed with a will-to-win spirit for he will never reach his full potential without it. Without the mental concentration on the urge to succeed, the determination to lift those weights with maximum speed, strength and ferocity, it will be difficult to exceed one's training performances.

Temperament has some bearing on this. The phlegmatic type of individual, with a stolid and unimaginative mind, does not find it easy to cultivate this keyed-up mentality and this type of competitor, generally, doesn't vary much in his training and competition performances.

On the other hand, we have the man whose mental make-up is such that he is stimulated to produce his best in competition. He is often highly-strung, with a mental attitude that is a driving force enabling him to produce a performance that is, to some extent, an abnormal one. His emotional state under the stress of competition brings out that something extra – something that he cannot do under normal training conditions.

Choosing Poundages

One of the most important aspects of weight-lifting competition is that of choosing the correct poundages for the various lifts and attempts.

With only three attempts permissible for each lift, it is essential not to make any mistakes. A wrong selection could mean that your best registered poundage is lower than need be, or even that no poundage at all will result.

The first few contests for a beginner should be experimental. Essentially they must be so, because until one has actually lifted in competition it is not possible to know just how one will react to it.

Experience must be gained. It is only experience that will teach you ; only experience that will enable you to know yourself and what kind of competitor you are likely to develop into.

It is a good thing to start off well ; to succeed with all your attempts. You need not be too ambitious or obsessed with the desire to win in your first few competitions. You want experience. You want to learn. So plan your lifts wisely. Take poundages that you are reasonably sure you can succeed with.

Normally when you enter a competition your aim is to win if possible. By this I mean your tactics will be planned to produce a winning total if you know you have some chance of winning. If the opposition is such that you have no chance, then your plans may be different. Your aim will be to improve on your previous best total, so that some progress can be seen.

The beginner's first competition will not, as a rule, be anything of importance. It may be a league contest, inter-club contest or a county championship, or just a friendly contest. And it should be regarded purely as a test piece.

First, let us consider your training immediately prior to the contest.

A heavy workout should be taken about a week beforehand, working up to your limit poundages. This will give you a good indication of your current form. Then have two more training sessions, the last one at least two or three days before the contest. Then relax completely until the time of the event.

In this way you will come to the platform rested and all ready and eager to tackle the weights. It is neither wise nor necessary to train right up to the day before the contest.

Your poundages in the contest should be chosen so that your third attempt is the best you have accomplished in training. In this way, it is most likely that you will succeed with all of your attempts – making a good psychological start to your weight-lifting career.

As an example, let's assume that your best training Press is 140 lb. Start in the competition with 125 lb. Then take 135 lb. for your second attempt, and finally the 140 lb.

It may be that all these weights will feel light, even your final attempt. If so, then this is a good sign, an indication that you may develop into a good competitive performer. On the other hand, you may fail with some of your lifts – particularly the third attempts.

Whatever happens, take a mental note of it for your future guidance.

Later, as you gain experience and improvement comes, your poundages will often have to be governed by your chances in the competition. Sometimes you may have to attempt a poundage that you have never succeeded with – or perhaps even attempted – before. More and more you will have to watch your chief rivals and the state of the competition.

If you have a good coach or adviser, then his help in this respect will be invaluable – as you are far more likely to do better if your mind is free to concentrate on tearing up the weights instead of also having to watch your prospects, poundages and tactical moves.

Do not be afraid to take chances, or to experiment. It is all experience. But you must learn from your experience. Remember how you reacted whenever you attempted any poundage that you had never lifted before. It is vitally important to have confidence whenever you do tackle personal-record poundages. Any half-belief in your ability, or hesitation at a vital stage of the lift, will mean failure.

Warming Up

Before the contest starts you will need to warm up both physically and mentally. Physically so that when you are ready for your first attempt on the platform your muscles will be warm, your circulatory system working at an increased tempo. Mentally so that your mind will be stimulated to produce your maximum effort.

Many individuals vary as to the extent and intensity of warming up required. Some function well in the competition with just a minimum of warming up, maybe just some free movements and a few light Presses and Snatches. Others do better with a more intensive programme, warming up for a longer period and working up to poundages just below what they intend to start with.

Only experience can prove what is needed for yourself. My personal preference is to devote a period of about twenty minutes to some freestanding movements followed by light to moderate Presses and Snatches, with the emphasis on speed and precision of movement and performing low repetitions and single lifts.

The work should be timed so that you have finished your warm-up just a few moments before taking your first competition lift.

Wear a track suit during this warming-up period. It is essential to keep the body warm during the whole period of the competition, right from the time you weigh-in to the final lift of the contest.

In between your lifts keep on your track suit and don't sit around too much, which will nullify to some extent the warming-up work you have done.

There is much more to weight lifting than employing the muscular force of the body. Of equal importance – or perhaps even greater – is the driving force of the mind. The emotional state must be such that the body is harnessed to produce maximum effort. With the mind in a normal state, not obsessed by any will-to-win, one's performance will not reach full potential. There must be determination, drive, eagerness and ambition. And this must, in many cases and to a large extent, be artificially created, depending on the individual.

Many athletes have a good measure of natural ability in this direction and, as the hour of the contest approaches, find themselves automatically building up a mental stimulus capable of producing their absolute best on the occasion. Others find it difficult, but must constantly endeavour to develop this quality. This means mind training as well as physical training.

Index

154